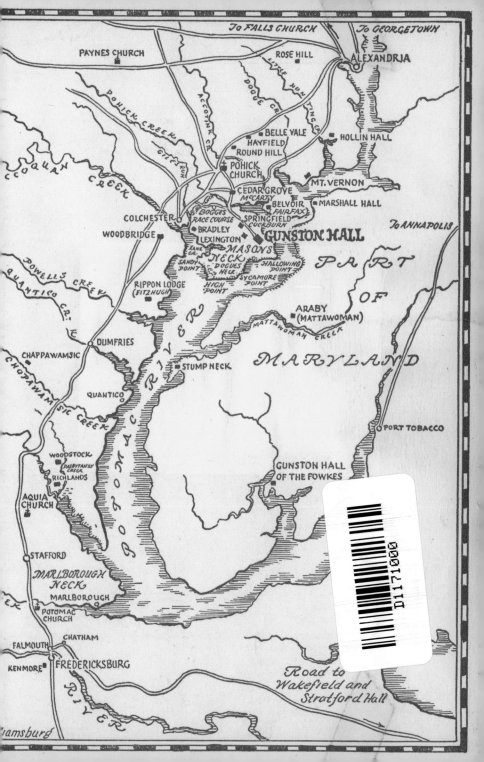

GLIMPSE OF GLORY

Presented By
The National Society
of the
Colonial Dames
of America
in the State of

Rhode Island

GEORGE MASON

From a portrait now in possession of Mrs. William Beverley Mason
of Washington, D. C. The artist is unknown. The canvas bears the
signature of George Mason on the back. Photograph by Victor Amato
of Washington, D. C.

ANN EILBECK MASON
From a portrait now in possession of Mrs. William Beverley Mason
of Washington. A second copy from the lost original by Hasselius.
Photograph by Victor Amato of Washington.

Glimpse of Glory

George Mason of Gunston Hall

BY

MARIAN BUCKLEY COX

Drawings by Elmo Jones

GARRETT & MASSIE, INCORPORATED
RICHMOND • VIRGINIA

124856

To My Husband

Thomas Riggs Cox

with whom I have learned to love the

land of his forefathers

Author's Foreword

This story of George Mason of Gunston Hall, his family, and the life which flowed through his house on the Potomac, is history in all its essentials. Fiction has been employed only to clothe the known facts with life. The fictitious characters are: the Fanshaws, mother and son; Colonel Mason's Enos and Liberty, the servants of Mrs. Graham and of Mrs. Mercer, the dogs and the roan mare.

It is the writer's belief that our national strength lies in observing the adage, "All for one and one for all." In that spirit, she believes that all the United States should join in appreciation of the Old Dominion's gifts to our entire land, that the distinguished sons of each state belong to the whole country and that George Mason, most self-forgetful of all our founding fathers, needs only to be known, to be greatly honored as one of the greatest of America's sons.

GUNSTON HALL TODAY

After the war between the north and south, Gunston Hall fell upon sad days. It passed out of the possession of the Mason family and into such a state of neglect that it served for a time as a logging camp. After many vicissitudes, during which its plantation houses vanished and architectural excrescences were built upon its graceful exterior, it became the home of Mr. and Mrs. Louis Hertle. Under their beneficent care the old house regained much of its original beauty. After Mrs. Hertle's death, Mr. Hertle, in accordance with her wishes, conveyed the title of Gunston Hall and of the now shrunken lands belonging to it, to the Commonwealth of Virginia. As Mrs. Hertle, who had been a member of The National Society of Colonial Dames of America had desired, a Board of Regents elected from this Society became its custodians. It was formally opened to the public in 1952 as a memorial to George Mason.

Gradually, Gunston Hall is being restored to its original beauty. Colonial Dames of the entire country have expended great effort and much study and research in its restoration. The wide hall, in the center of the house, opens upon a distant view of the Potomac. The river is seen framed by an allée of box-wood 200 years old. The bushes were undoubtedly planted by Mason's order. They are twelve feet high and the walk they border is two hundred and fifty feet long. On each side of the allée, formal gardens stretch out in incredible beauty, and below the terraces lies the "Long Level"—the tip of the Peninsula. It is a wild tumbled woodland where the red deer still dwell as they did in Mason's day.

The way to Gunston Hall is plainly marked. The traveller may come to it by turning off the Shirley Highway upon Route 242, or by Route 1, which was once the Publick Road and, earlier still, the King's Highway.

MARIAN BUCKLEY COX

Member for the State of New York on the Board of Regents of Gunston Hall, appointed by the Governor of Virginia from The National Society of Colonial Dames in America.

Introduction

On Wednesday, June 23, 1779, the flagship *Sensible*, a French frigate of 36 guns, under Captain Chavagnes, was at half sail on a choppy sea six days out, enroute from France to America. To starboard and to larboard were the *Bonhomme Richard* of 42 guns, under Captain John Paul Jones, and the *Alliance*, under Captain Landais. In the convoy were three other able ships of the line, well gunned. To complete the convoy were two ill-constructed and aggravating tubs whose sails seemed to ship more water than wind. Five knots in a fair wind was about all they could do. Trailing the convoy since the preceding Saturday were from two to six English privateers yearning for, yet fearing, the chance to close in for the kill. A few shots across their bows discouraged cordiality. On Tuesday night they had peeled off to be seen no more.

Aboard the *Sensible* was a French Commission deputed to a fledging nation in the throes of the birth of freedom under the laws of God and man. Aboard also was John Adams and his twelve year old son, John Quincy. The cargoes of human flesh and sinews of war were the answer of France to the subtle yet fervent plea of the Declaration of Independence. Thomas Jefferson, John Adams, Benjamin Franklin, Robert Livingston and Roger Sherman had pieced together the Declaration of Independence from the products of American minds and the sentiments of the day and had deposited it in the laps of the Gods as a hopeful prayer for aid in the American struggle for life over death.

Something about the sea, the mission, and the great part John Adams had played and was yet playing, lifted him out of himself. At no hour of life had he felt so near the ideal of independence towards which American patriots had staggered so long, to find always beyond reach. The danger of capture at sea was now past. Something less than relaxed conversation would have been out of place. Something less than sincerity would have been a travesty on the *Sensible* that day.

M. Marbois, Secretary of the French Commission, fell into easy conversation with Adams on deck during the afternoon of that Wednesday. In that conversation John Adams told a few secrets that the world has either overlooked or ignored. After the evening meal, the second future President of the United States put John Quincy, the sixth future President, to bed in his hammock and then retired to his nearby cabin. The conversation of the afternoon was rebounding in his mind. Soliloquy tortured him. "Philadelphia" haunted him and drove sleep westward many knots. As the *Sensible* seemed to slumber, John Adams recorded in his diary a portion of the conversation with Marbois: Here is a part:

"All religions are tolerated in America", said M. Marbois; "and the ambassadors have in all courts a right to a chapel in their own way; but Mr. Franklin never had any." "No," said I, laughing, "because Mr. Franklin had no"—I was going to say what I did not say, and will not say here. I stopped short, and laughed. "No," said M. Marbois; "Mr. Franklin adores only great Nature, which has interested a great many people of both sexes in his favor." "Yes," said I, laughing, "all the atheists, deists and libertines, as well as the philosophers and ladies, are in his train,—another Voltaire, and thence—" "Yes," said M. Marbois, "he is celebrated as the great philosopher and the great legislator of America." "He is," said I, "a great philosopher, but as a legislator of America he has done very little. It is universally believed in France, England, and all Europe, that his electric wand has accomplished all this revolution. But nothing is more groundless. He has done very little. It is believed that he made all the American constitutions and their confederation; but he made neither. He did not even make the constitution of Pennsylvania, bad as it is. The bill of rights is taken almost verbatim from that of Virginia which was made and published two or three months before that of Philadelphia was begun; it was made by Mr. Mason . . ."

That of "Philadelphia" (meaning Pennsylvania) "was begun" in late August, 1776. The original draft of "that of Virginia—made by Mr. Mason" reached Richard Henry Lee in Philadelphia, in the handwriting of Mason, in late May, 1776. It appeared in the June 1st issue of the *Virginia Gazette* which reached Philadelphia four days later. On June 6th, it reappeared in the *Pennsylvania Evening Post*. On the 12th it reappeared in the *Pennsylvania Gazette*. The first paragraph was:

"That all men are born equally free and independent, and have certain inherent natural Rights, of which they cannot, by any Compact, deprive, or divest their Posterity; among which are the Enjoyment of Life and Liberty, with the Means of acquiring and possessing Property, and pursuing and Obtaining Happiness and Safety."

Franklin, the philosopher, was unwilling to deface those lines that firmed for the ages the profound wisdom of the Cato of his country. He copied Mason's words "almost verbatim" into the Pennsylvania Declaration of Rights.

Adams could not remember the first name, "George", so he let it go as "Mr. Mason". Seventy-five years later Charles Francis Adams, son of John Quincy and grandson of John, could remember neither the first nor the last name. Nevertheless he recorded in the *Works of John Adams*, Vol. 4, page 220, et. seq., that his grandfather had no sooner disembarked from the *Sensible* to embrace his wife, grandmother of Charles Francis, than he was called away to write the Massachusetts Declaration of Rights. The grandson disclosed that in August 1779 his grandfather did exactly what Benjamin Franklin did in August, 1776. He too copied "almost verbatim' from the Virginia Declaration of Rights. Had Charles Francis Adams looked a little closer his footnotes might well have been much more enlightening.

It was in the month of June, 1776 that John Adams, Benjamin Franklin and Thomas Jefferson were in Philadelphia struggling to compose the Declaration of Independence. It was easy enough to catalogue the sins of George III. That had been done by many others many times. The South Carolina Constitution of March 1776 and Judge William Henry Drayton's charge to a grand jury at Charleston, S. C., in April 1776, were certainly models that were copied from. But their combined wisdom was not equal to the task of framing a powerful preamble justifying revolution, with an appeal to the hearts, the reason and the sense of justice of all men. Nothing like that had ever been penned by man. Finally they saw the manuscript in the hands of Richard Henry Lee and later saw it in the newspapers. *Eureka! Eureka! Eureka!* "Where did Mason get it?" No one knew. Richard Henry Lee knew the man of Gunston Hall better than any other in Philadelphia so he was appealed to. Here is the answer reported by Jefferson in a letter to Madison near a half century later:

"Richard Henry Lee charged it as copied from Locke's treatise on government."

That was just one other time when Richard guessed wrong. George Mason was a prophet. Like Ezekiel, he had learned the gift of prophecy from the "roll of a book", multiplied thousands of times. In his ample library at Gunston Hall he had filtered five thousand years of history. The principles of the Virginia Declaration of Rights were the distilled essence of history's bitter fruits gathered from her Gardens of Gethsemene.

Revealing as the *John Adams Diary* was, it did not tell all. It did not concede that the Preamble to the Declaration of Independence was but a slight variant of the first three paragraphs of Mason's Declaration of Rights. The variance substituted the specious doctrine of *equality of birth* for the common sense doctrine of *equality of freedom and independence*. It also substituted a fruitless "pursuit of happiness" for the ownership of property and attainment of happiness. The "pursuit of happiness" is but vain drudgery if it is not to be obtained. "Happiness and safety" may not be obtained in this world without the lawful "means of acquiring and possessing property."

Franklin and Adams consented to deface Mason's words in their appeal to France in the Declaration of Independence, but they were unwilling to deface them as a rule of life for Pennsylvania and Massachusetts. The Declaration of Independence was written as an appeal to the simple-minded peasants and philosophers of France. Those who prepared it knew that it would never breathe the first breath as living law in America—and it never has. The Mason concept became living law in every American constitution and is now in every world constitution except Russia, Mongolia, Ukraine and Guatemala. Disillusioned France struck the doctrine of unbounded *equality* from her motto in 1940 and from her Declaration of Rights in 1946. *Equality* cannot thrive in free soil. It thrives only in the sewers of Slavic slavery.

Alexander Hamilton expressed the idea well on the floor of the Constitutional Convention in Philadelphia on June 26, 1787: "Inequality will exist as long as liberty exists. It unavoidably results from that very liberty itself." Equality beyond the range of legal rights is despotic restraint. Liberty wears no chains. Equality homogenizes so that cream no longer rises to the top. It puts the eagle in the henhouse that he may no longer soar.

Who was the "legislator of America"? His name was "Mr. Mason" aboard the *Sensible* in 1779. John Adams seemed never able to remember even that much of his name again. The biographers of Adams, Franklin and Jefferson have likewise suffered equal lapse of memory.

George Mason was a delegate to the Constitutional Convention in Philadelphia in 1787. He refused to sign a proposed constitution that sanctioned human slavery and omitted the rights of men. The first six words of his *Objection* were heard in every hovel and on every frontier of America: "There is no Declaration of Rights"! He carried his deathless struggle for a Federal Bill of Rights to the people, and lived barely long enough to see his efforts crowned with victory and his name drowned in oblivion, because of the bitterness engendered in that struggle. Something about the man and his story sounds like a play back of a few tragic scenes of history, along the road to the Cross, and to Tower Hill.

Liberty must have her martyrs in every age. It is blood drained from their veins and abuse heaped upon them that neutralizes arbitrary power in governments and reasserts man's natural right to be let alone. Martyrs to human liberty and dignity are those who think in terms of ages gone and to come—ancestry and posterity. Mason thought of the ages while others thought of the hour.

In October, 1792 George Mason was buried at the edge of an old field near Gunston Hall. His body was placed as close to the side of Ann, the wife of his youth and mother of his children, as her tomb would permit. He wanted it that way. Her tomb thus became his own. For 19 years his heart had been there anyway.

On the following day the five sons and four daughters gathered in the library of Gunston Hall for the reading of his solemn will. It had been written in 1773, just after the death of Ann and before the Revolution had begun. One paragraph of that will mirrored the man:

> "I recommend it to my sons from my own experience in life, to prefer the happiness of independence and a private station to the troubles and vexation of publick business, but if either their own inclinations or the necessity of the times should engage them in public affairs, I charge them on a father's blessing never to let the motives of private interest or ambition induce them to betray, nor the terrors of poverty and disgrace, or the fear of danger or of death, deter them from asserting the liberty of their country and endeavoring to transmit to their posterity those sacred rights to which themselves were born."

Abnegation of self is not a creed. It is not a philosophy. It is a *way of life*. Narrow is its way and strait is its gate. Those who travel that way find few vistas from which to look down for a glimpse of mundane glory. Their vistas lie straight ahead and up. *Straight ahead*, is in any and all directions unless the course is set by that from whence we came. The first is philosophy. The other is experience. That is the chief reason why no frame of government has ever survived whose architect was a philosopher. The light of experience is never shed upon Utopias. Such are not in the vistas of evolution's pioneers. Such are not in the vistas of the martyrs to human liberty and dignity. The crowns they wear are of thorns. The garlands they bear are crosses. They don't stand in marble on public squares. Had it been tinseled garlands they sought, they would not have travelled the narrow way and entered the strait gate.

In this book Gunston Hall becomes warm again. The boxwood out front, planted by George Mason near 200 years ago, no longer stand twelve feet high as in 1954. They are dwarfed to six inches as the newlywed master of Gunston Hall plants then under the gentle and effective undersight of Ann. The cherry trees resume their pattern. George Washington and other neighbors and friends listen intently to the humble sage of the Potomac who could see to the bottom of every proposition at one glance.

Here Mrs. Thomas Riggs Cox recaptures enough of reality to relate history. She dresses George Mason in fiction in order that we may walk with him and talk with him. In her book we feel his strong arms about us, and hear the beating of his loving heart. The father of the Bill of Rights and the wisest statesman America has ever known becomes the gracious host again.

R. CARTER PITTMAN.

Dalton, Georgia.
August 6, 1954.

GLIMPSE OF GLORY

Prologue

Today, an old house sits dreaming. Its memories reach far back into America's past, and as the old do, it remembers best and most happily, its early years. Many visitors come and go, but they make little impression upon the ancient dwelling of Colonel George Mason. It is of the Colonel and his beautiful Lady, and of their children, that the house thinks now. Those were such happy days!

The house feels again the warmth of open fires in winter, and savors again in summer the fragrance of Persian jessamine and guelder rose, hears the liquid joyous laughter of George Mason's beautiful Lady, Ann, Mistress Mason, and of their nine children. There is the bell-like cry of the hounds to remember, too, the song of the mockingbird, the call of the whippoorwill, and in early spring, the staccato barking of the foxes in the then nearby woods, and the chorus of peepers along the margins of Pohick Creek, the Potomac and the Occoquan. Most heart warming of all the night sounds was the haunting minor melody of the negro "Hymn Tunes."

There were gay evenings once at Gunston Hall, card games in the drawing room, sumptuous dinners, served with great ceremony in the dining room, and dancing in the hall. The fiddlers used to play in the little musicians' gallery at the head of the stairs while the planters and their ladies stepped to marches, measured minuets and the Sir Roger de Coverley.

Best of all, there were children's dancing classes when the dancing master came, and equipages from neighboring plantations rolled up the drive with the children from other great houses. Sometimes the children came by water in barges which delivered their precious cargo at the landing below the garden. The gay children, in powdered hair and miniature gowns with flowered panniers and quilted petticoats, or knee breeches and with silver buckles on their shoes, are among the old house's dearest memories. No wonder Gunston Hall is too busy with its thoughts to notice us today!

[1]

Modern admirers speak of brick laid in Flemish bond, of a porch, Palladian in derivation, of the Chinese Chippendale Room, the only one of its kind in Virginia, or of the Palladian Room, said to be the most important example of carved decoration of its period in this country.[1] Architects are charmed with the hall's double arch and the fluted balusters of the stair. Of all this praise, however, the house remains unaware. Its brick, rosy with color of the Virginia clay, seems to glow with the sunlight and warmth of another day.

Turn back then, if you would see Gunston Hall live again, and with this ancient dwelling, try to see the men and women, boys and girls, and little children, with their negroes, dogs and horses; and catch if you can, the sound of fiddle and hunting horn, the laughter and the weeping, and most of all, the *glimpse of glory* in our country's future—that hope which gave courage to our forefathers.

1

IN THE CITY of Washington, upon a corner of the building which houses the National Archives of the United States, the traveller may read this legend: "What is past is prologue." It is in England's past and at the Battle of Worcester that we pick up the prologue and the first threads of our tale.

The Stuart prince who later became Charles II, had swept down from Scotland in the summer of 1651 with 16,000 men, mostly Scots. In England, those cavaliers who were loyal to the memory of Charles I, "the Martyr King", rallied to the banner of his son. Their number was disappointingly small and Cromwell, with his well trained army, brought the king and his royalists to bay at Worcester, the ancient city of the west country near the borders of Wales. Here, on the 3rd of September, Charles met crushing defeat. Of his followers, three thousand of his men lay dead upon the field of battle and ten thousand were prisoners of the Parliamentarians. Of those who escaped, most took the roads to the northwest where deep friendly forests and kindly country people offered their only hope of safety.

Among these hopeless cavaliers, now refugees from the power of Cromwell, we see three whose descendants were destined to play a part in the shaping of a new world. One, a young man in his early twenties, was obviously an unhorsed captain of cavalry. With him was a younger man who, judging from his close resemblance to the captain, was his brother. Captain George

Mason and William Mason supported between them a wounded older man, Colonel Gerard Fowke of Breewood[2] Hall in the Parish of Breewood near Wolverhampton, Staffordshire. The Mason brothers were his friends and neighbors; their home, Gunston Hall, was in the same Parish.

Their halting journey, hiding by day and making their painful way by night, brought them at last to the humble cottage of a woodcutter in the vicinity of Breewood. The good man's wife had been nurse to Captain Mason, his brother, and his sisters. Here they were safe, and it was not the first time that the deep forests of the west country had hidden refugees from England's political turmoil. Here Colonel Fowke's son found them. He and his wife had passage from Bristol. It was arranged that they would take Captain Mason's young wife with them, disguised as Mistress Fowke's maid, and Captain Mason and his brother would join them at Norfolk, Virginia, when they could. Colonel Fowke, once gentleman of the bedchamber to his sovereign Charles I, would stay and take his luck under Cromwell.[3] Perchance the tide would turn. He would do his utmost to hold the estates of Gunston and Breewood Hall for the young men's return.

George Mason and his brother found themselves at length passed from one loyal countryman to another and finally, long after Mistress Mason had left for America, abroad a great winged ship sailing from Bristol to Norfolk, Virginia. As Lands End faded behind them into the morning sea-mist, that prophetic quality in the soul of man told Captain Mason that, for him, England was indeed gone. Only a sunlit sky and a seemingly endless expanse of water appeared to lie ahead—but beyond, he knew, was his gallant wife, the children who would be born and a new world to be carved from a wilderness. Our story is not of these first Masons, but let us have one last glimpse of this first American George Mason in his Virginia home. His house was of wood. Built upon the lines of a simple English cottage of that day, it had two rooms only. The large raftered room at one end served as kitchen and dining hall. The smaller room which opened off it, was the bedroom. A large fireplace at each end warmed the house. It was built upon a neck of land running out into the Potomac. The place was known as Accohick and is about ten miles from the present city of Fredericksburg, Virginia. The point of land came, in later days, to be known as Marlborough or Potomac Point, but on the night of which we speak, all those names were still unknown. The little house was a cabin in a vast wilderness. The forest was full of savage red men and wild animals. The half circle of firelight on the hearth seemed the extent of the civilized world. Captain Mason sat upon a rude wooden bench facing his wife. His hair, in the fashion of the cavaliers, fell curling darkly on his shoulders. He was smoking the already popular tobacco in a long pipe. His wife, a charming blonde English woman, held their small son, the second George Mason, in her arms. She had placed an empty wooden bowl on the floor beside her. The baby, full of vension soup, was playing contentedly with a locket which hung by a gold chain around his mother's neck. This locket, which was of gold, was his mother's greatest treasure. A few similar ones may be seen in England to-day. When not upon Mistress Mason's neck, it was kept in a smooth leather case into which it fitted exactly. It contained a miniature of the martyr King and, most wonderful and enchanting to the little boy, there were three transparencies which, fitted into the gold frame over the face of the king and showed Charles, first wearing his crown, next without his crown and then beheaded with blood pouring from his severed neck and his hair clutched in the fist of the executioner.[4]

As the baby played with his mother's weird bauble, the captain and his lady talked quietly of the home they had left and of their changed estate. They had left the young William Mason in Norfolk and had taken up land far to the north on the Potomac river—"Potowmack" they pronounced it. Mary spoke often of the Fowkes. They had settled near the Masons at Pasbytanzy and both Masons and Fowkes were glad of the Catholic family of Brents who, after a quarrel with the Calverts in Maryland, had moved down to Virginia and settled on land they called

"Richlands," further up Aquia Creek, which flowed into the Potomac near the Mason dwelling. George Mason leaned forward and knocked the bowl of his pipe gently against the iron pot which hung near him on a crane over the fire.

"I think," he said, "that my father would have been glad to see us here. I used to love to listen, when I was a little shaver, to tales of his adventures here in Virginia when he was a young man and sailed with the gentlemen adventurers far up the Chesapeake.[5] I believe he would have settled here himself if my mother had been willing, but she loved her Fowke relatives and her home in Staffordshire."

Mary's eyes filled with tears at the mention of home and he added hastily to remind her they had had no choice. "Ah, well —it took a revolution to dislodge us, but here we are."

He lifted the sturdy little George from his mother's arms. The baby clung for a moment to the miniature of the martyr King as if, like his mother, he relinquished England with regret. When his father tossed him to the rafters, however, he gurgled with delight and his father, cradling him fondly, exclaimed: "And you, my son, will be, not a cavalier, but an Indian fighter and a Virginian!"

George Mason and his Mary lived and died and were buried, according to the old records,[6] "at Accohick near Pasbytanzy." True to his father's prophecy, the sturdy little boy became a doughty Indian fighter. Like his father, he became successively a captain, a major, and a colonel and His Majesty's Justice of the Peace, with almost entire control of the affairs of the county.[7] And, like his father before him, he was finally appointed County Lieutenant or Commander of Plantations. The County Lieutenant commanded the militia with the rank of Colonel, was entitled to a seat in the Council and, as such, was a Judge of the General Court. He was appointed directly by the Governor and was the possessor of very large powers in the civil and military control of the county. He presided over the County Courts at the head of the justices.[8]

There is a tradition in the Mason family that it was they who named Stafford County in Virginia for their loved Staffordshire at home. Certain it is that George Mason II strengthened his Staffordshire ties when he lost his heart to Mary Fowke, the daughter of his father's friend. He sold the old dwelling house at Accohick with all the "houses, out-houses, barns, stables, tobacco houses and all other edifices" on the place, reserving the tomb of Colonel George Mason and "the Burying Place on which it stands . . . to be and to remain to the said George Mason and to his heirs forever."[9]

He moved further up the Potomac and in 1696 we find him acquiring 2,109 acres of land "between the Potomac and Occoquan Rivers called 'Doeg's Island.' "[10] Evenutally the Masons acquired the whole of Dogue's Neck as well as more land to the north running as far up the river as the present Georgetown. Before his death in 1716, he had become a great land owner. Land was the wealth of the eighteenth century planters and they were constantly buying and selling it.

Like the 2nd George Mason, the 2nd Gerard Fowke moved up the river also. He settled upon the Maryland side of the Potomac and named his house, which is described as a "substantial mansion,"[11] Gunston Hall. Although the original house is gone, his descendants continue to live to this day[12] in a house upon the same land.

The second George Mason married three times.[13] By Mary Fowke he had five children; the eldest was the third American George Mason. His three groups of children grew up in what came later to be called, the "Old Plantation," near the river's edge on Dogue's Neck.

The third George Mason was perhaps the most charming of the early Masons. Glamorous, that currently much used word to describe a shining personality, seems most applicable to this wealthy and charming young planter. Our first vivid glimpse of him is as a Knight of the "Golden Horse Shoe." He accompanied Governor Spotswood in 1716 on that party of "gay and gallant gentlemen who formed the governor's escort"[14] to Virginia's western hills to encourage English exploration of the

west. Each cavalier was given a small gold horseshoe pin studded
with jewels to represent nails. Horses went unshod on the soft
soil of the Tidewater Country and the horseshoe, so necessary
in the rocky hills, was therefore taken as a symbol for this
debonair order of Knighthood. In time, these little golden pins
became valued family heirlooms.

George Mason III held the same titles and performed the
same duties as his father and grandfather. He made his first
appearance in the Assembly in 1718. He and his brother-in-law,
George Fitzhugh, represented Stafford County and in 1719 he
was appointed by the governor to the high position of County
Lieutenant of Stafford.

Trade between Glasgow in Scotland, and the growing town
of Dumfries on the Occoquan, not far from Dogue's Neck,
increased greatly during the lifetime of George Mason III. As
County Lieutenant, Mason was in a position to extend to the
merchants courtesies which greatly promoted trade. As a token
of the Scots' appreciation, Mason was given in 1720, the freedom of the City of Glasgow, and, as proof of this, he received
a Burgess Ticket which was a richly illuminated manuscript
admitting him as, "Received Burgess and Guild brother of this
City."

The following year Colonel Mason married Ann Thomson.
This lady was later described by the Masons' friend and rector,
the Reverend John Moncure, in these words: "She was a good
woman, a great woman and a lovely woman."

Certain it is that there were many who wished to marry her.
She was the daughter of Stevens Thomson who, during the
reign of Queen Anne, had been Attorney General for Virginia.
He came of a Yorkshire family and like his father before him,
Stevens Thomson had taken his AB at Cambridge and was ad-
mitted to the Middle Temple for the study of law. His father's
distinguished career influenced the queen to authorize Governor
Nicholson of Virginia to appoint Stevens Thomson her Majesty's
Attorney General in Virginia. And here we find his good, beauti-
ful and intelligent little daughter much sought after by all the

young gallants of an increasingly prosperous society.

Young Mason, already a widower and with no children, entered the lists to try for her hand. He met with success in love, as indeed he did in all he undertook. Ann Stevens Thomson became Mrs. George Mason III and of the many children born, three survived, George Mason IV, the subject of our story, a little girl whom they named Mary, and a boy called Thomson for his mother's people. George Mason moved his family from Virginia, across the river to the Maryland side of the Potomac.[15] Here he owned land on Chickamuxen Creek in Charles County. The river seemed no barrier to eighteenth century Virginians. It was a highway between the planters' estates, and Mason was as much at home in a boat upon its surface as he was upon its shores, where his father and grandfather had tramped and hunted around every bay and inlet.

Nevertheless, When George Mason IV was ten years old, Mary four, and little Thomson two, their father's sailboat was overturned in a sudden squall and a brilliant career was suddenly cut off. Like a shooting star which vanishes from sight at the top of its arc, Colonel Mason vanished from sight at the height of his career.

2

ONE SPRING MORNING in 1736, in the drawing room of Mr. John Mercer's home at Marlborough on Potomac Neck, two boys stood side by side in the deep embrasure of a window. They looked out upon a rainy day, a dripping garden of box, crape myrtle, periwinkle and ivy, and beyond, to the lazy silver Potomac. One small boy, in red coat and buff knee breeches, had dark wavy hair tied back with a ribbon. The other, a small negro, had a round, close-cropped head and a singularly pleasant round face. His skin was of a rich brown color and he was dressed in the blue livery of the Masons.[16]

Obviously they were a young gentleman and his equally young servant. Obviously also they were two small boys whose nefarious plans for the day had been spoiled by the weather. The boy in the red coat was George Mason, aged ten years, the other, his boy Enos, exactly the same age, the two having been born upon the same night. Enos was talking:

"Nebba you mind, Massa Geoge. It mot clear, an' I'll take off dis coat an' go find me a lot of warms. Late dis evenin' we'll go fishin'. I'll show you de place I saw a water moccasin swim across our old fish hole."

George's eyes filled with pleasure.

"Fine, Enos," he said. "You do that and we'll go fishin' sure enough this evenin'. I'd like to get that moccasin skin before we go home. Is he as big as the rattler we caught last Autumn?"

Here the boys were interrupted by their discovery of Mr. Williams' presence in the room. The Scottish tutor had entered unheard, and stood thoughtfully regarding Mr. Mercer's fine collection of books. These were kept upon the shelves of the two cupboards which flanked the chimney piece, one upon either side. Young Williams had opened one of the doors and George moved over to join him as Enos vanished.

Mr. Williams, a slim, attractive young Scotsman, had arrived recently, and was still pale and thin after a five weeks, stormy voyage from Glasgow. Nevertheless, he considered himself fortunate to have been brought over by a family which was well known for its promotion of trade between the mother country and Virginia. George Mason, whose London factor had engaged Williams as a tutor for young George, was well known, both in London and in Glasgow. He was considered a keen and honorable business man. It was said also, that he came from an ancient Warwickshire family. Williams understood that the first American Mason had fled from England after the battle of Worcester, when so many cavaliers gave their lives for their king, or went into exile. When Charles II regained his father's lost crown, the Masons had been already well settled in Virginia, English country gentlemen still, but having suffered a "sea change."

Upon his arrival in the colony, Mr. Williams was shocked to discover that Mr. Mason had lost his life in an overturned sailboat on the Potomac. On his arrival in the bereaved household, Williams had been deeply moved by Mrs. Mason's courage and fortitude. He had found the small family in the midst of moving back from the Maryland to the Virginia side of the Potomac, but in spite of the confusion of the moment, Mrs. Mason's welcome had been warm and gracious. There on the landing, below the now deserted Maryland house, it was she who explained their tragic circumstance, making the new tutor feel she would count upon his help.

Today, he looked fondly at the little figure by his side. There had been no question of lessons in those first days of his arrival.

The move back to Chappawamsic in Virginia, Mrs. Mason's home by her dower right under her husband's will, had required much help of the new tutor and of George. Even with many negroes to wait on them and countless and ever present relatives and friends, there had been innumerable tasks for the new tutor and his charge to perform. Williams had found himself deeply sympathetic with a small boy who tried so earnestly to fill his father's place and to comfort his widowed mother, small sister and two-year-old brother.

Chappawamsic[17] was a comfortable little stone house built upon high land. Already it showed signs of the beauty and charm with which its mistress would endow it. Williams would always remember one evening when Mrs. Mason, weary and anxious with her new responsibilities, had sent for him. He had found her by the fire in the little parlor, her workbasket heaped high with small clothes to be looked over and given to brown Nan Old Gate[18] for mending on the morrow. Williams had noticed that her beautiful eyes were swimming in tears. Making no effort to hide them Mrs. Mason had bade him sit down, motioning him to draw a chair near her.

It appeared that, under her husband's will, she was not the sole guardian of her children, but that her husband's kinsman, Mr. John Mercer of Marlborough, was co-guardian. This gentleman was young George's uncle, having married Mr. Mason's pretty sister, Catherine.

"A most brilliant Scotsman," Mrs. Mason said, "and a very fine one, but short of temper and given, in rage, to a picturesque form of speech."

"I feel," she continued, "that George has been too much under the shadow of my sorrow. He is a very sympathetic boy, and I feel that he should go down, under your care, to Mr. and Mrs. Mercer for a few weeks. One of the ships from Dumfries is stopping at our wharf tomorrow. She will stop at Marlborough and it is my wish that you and George sail on her to Mr. Mercer's. You will find there a remarkably fine library and it will be a good opportunity to awaken George's interest in the delights of study. Mr. Mercer is a student of history and a classical scholar. I am sure he will be willing to lend some of his books for George's further study on your return."

And so we see them at Marlborough on a rainy morning, considering the contents of one of the two book cupboards set in the panelling of the green drawing room. Young Williams' delighted gaze took in *Montaigne's Essays, Raleigh's History of the World, Malcolm on Music, Davidson's Virgil, Locke's Works, Sidney on Government, Chaucer's Tales, Hawkins' Crown Law, Salmon's History of England,* and many more.[19]

Anxious to enlist his pupil's interest, he asked, "What shall we read today, George?" Williams looked with pleasure at his pupil's aware and intelligent face. George was a well-knit boy with a high intellectual forehead, hazel eyes which sometimes changed to gray, and a cleft, firm chin. On the ride across the field from Chappawamsic to Dumfries Wharf, Williams had noted that George was already a good horseman, and that he had showed consideration for his horse, as well as skill in handling him. Later, on the boat, he had exhibited a wide-awake interest in all that went on, in the expert loading of the casks of tobacco taken aboard at Dumfries, the timing of their departure on the ebb tide, and the handling of the sails.

Now, Williams observed, he was all concentrated interest in the calfbound volumes before him. He looked up at his tutor with one of his engaging smiles, and said: "Oh, please Sir, may it be history, English history, and let's start at the beginning!"

And so it was history. Clouds darkened the pleasant green-panelled room. The fragrance of wet box came in at the windows, and the river, below the garden terraces, was shut out from view by the rain. The fire crackled pleasantly on the hearth, dispelling the dampness, but young Williams and his pupil were hardly aware of their surroundings.

Before the boy's fascinated inward eye the pageant of English history started to roll by, the story of his own race. He saw wave upon wave of invaders lose their identity on the island they came to conquer and stayed to enrich. He suffered with the de-

feated, and triumphed with the victors. The vanquished Harold
seemed unbearably tragic, until his conquered Saxon soldiers
triumphed ultimately in the flower of their race, Matilda, the
auburn haired princess of their royal line. George saw her win,
from her dour Norman husband, the rights of free men for her
own oppressed people. With swelling throat and moistened eye,
he listened as Mr. Williams filled in between the lines of Salmon's *History of England.* And tutor and pupil thrilled together
over the dramatic story of how Matilda gave to England the
Saxon Charter, a century before King John signed the Magna
Carta at Runnymede.

Later they would read together the story of James II's un-
popular reign, followed as it was by the English Bill of Rights,
written by Somers to be given to the English people by William
of Orange.

All this and more he would study later, and all he would
discuss with that provocative gentleman, his guardian, Mr. John
Mercer, and finally, in the years far ahead, he would add his own
great contribution of a Bill of Rights for a nation which on that
rainy morning in 1736, was still unborn. Today in Mrs. Mercer's peaceful drawing room that moment lay far in the future.
The tapestry of English history was torn aside by old Alpheus an-
nouncing dinner, and by the appearance in the doorway of his
uncle with pretty Aunt Catherine beside him, smiling. Danes,
Saxons and Normans were banished in a twinkling by the fragrance of one of Aunt Sally's wonderful dinners.

It was a pleasant group that gathered about the long table in
Mr. Mercer's wide hall. Dining rooms had not yet become
fashionable in Virginia, nor indeed in England, at that time, and
the family sat around a long and heavy oak table in the hall.
At the end of the hall a double door looked out upon the river.
This door opened down the centre from the top to bottom and
was thrown wide so that George could see, as he ate his dinner,
that the sunlight was breaking through the clouds. The guests
at his aunt and uncle's table were cousins and friends but they
interested our small boy not at all. His uncle was ponderously

discussing the Virginia charter with Mr. Moncure and Mr. Carter from "Clives," and George, who had eaten his mutton pie, thought they would never finish. His mind was upon the fishing expedition on which he was eager to set out with Enos. At last he caught his aunt's eye and at her nod of permission, he slipped noiselessly from his place, quite unobserved by Mr. Williams, who was interested in Mr. Mercer's conversation. Once safe in Aunt Sally's great earth-floored kitchen, he was reunited with Enos and the two vanished with incredible speed toward Aquia Creek and a safe, flat-bottomed boat pulled up on the sandy shore. Once in the boat they pushed up stream, fishing rods in hand and a long happy afternoon ahead. The fish were not biting. Sated with insect life brought down to the stream by the recent rains, they disdained the boys' worms and it was with all the thrill of adventure that the fishermen turned to a snake hunt. Pushing their boat into a small stream, tributary to the Aquia, they went in search of the deadly water moccasin whose haunts Enos was sure he knew. They were now upon the land where George's great-grandfather had settled. The cottage, as it had come to be called, was still there and the boys clambered ashore on the brokendown wharf. It was here in the rushes at the side of the wharf that they met the enemy and fell upon him with sticks and stones. George had seen a horesman snap a snake as he would his whip and break the reptile's neck and, leaning over, he grasped the dying creature's tail when, suddenly, Enos lunged against him and both boys stumbled frantically up the bank, George furious at the unexpected assault. Then he saw the reason. The moccasin's mate had been under the plank on which he was standing. It had coiled and struck but, due to Enos' quick action, it had missed. The angry words died on George's lips and the boys watched, spellbound, as a long, shining black shape disappeared into the rushes. They were not to be cheated of their kill, however, and lifting the dead moccasin with a stick, they threw it into their boat and started for home.

As they returned to the sandy beach at Marlborough the flutter of a little blue skirt caught George's eye. "That's Miss

Sally, Mrs. Brent's little girl," Enos said. "I heard hosses comin'
through the wood road when we was goin' out." Sure enough,
a small homely little girl of about six, in a long blue frock, stood
waiting on the beach. She had a tiptilted, freckled nose and
straight brown hair cut in a bang across her forehead. Sally
Brent was no beauty by the standards of her day. It was, however, a pleasant and alert little face she lifted to George Mason's
as he leaped ashore. "George," she cried, "they're all looking for
you and Mr. Williams is so mad, his face is dark red! You're
goin' to catch it! I came to tell you."

"Thank you, Sally, but you'll probably catch it too if you don't
run back," George said.

Sally, seeing the snake, shrank visibly but suppressed a little
squeak of fear and, with a wary eye on the black horror dangling
from George's hand, she followed him toward the house and
certain punishment. Her dark Bermudian mother,[20] who had
Spanish as well as English forebears, stood in the doorway behind
the glowering Mr. Mercer. George took the precaution to stow
his prized trophy in the crotch of a great tree where he could
retrieve and skin it later. Enos vanished toward the negro
quarters, while the young hunter and the small girl continued
their unhappy way to the house.

An hour later found George in solitary confinement after a
caning from his uncle. The boy whose disappearance had occasioned so much concern to the family at Marlborough, was
now shut in the room he shared with his tutor. In the future
he would ask Mr. Williams' permission before setting forth on a
fishing expedition. From the window of his room he watched
little Sarah Brent's departure for Woodstock, her father's home
further up Aquia Creek. She was mounted behind her mother
on a tall brown horse. An armed white servant rode behind
them. No doubt she would be punished too, for running down
to the shore to warn him of impending trouble. Her mother was
a severe and frightening woman. George noticed that Mistress
Brent, instead of flicking her horse lightly with her whip, as his
mother did, brought her crop down cruelly on the animal's flank

so that he snorted and leaped forward, and horses and riders vanished into the deep forest beyond the garden enclosure. The plain little girl in the blue frock was soon forgotten, not to appear again in his life for many a long day.

3

On a winter morning in 1750, a haze hung over the river at Dogue's Neck for the sun had just risen. Smoke curled from the two tall chimneys which flanked each end of a pink brick house built close to the water's edge, upon a bank considerably higher than its surroundings. The only living creature in sight was an old foxhound who was happily investigating the rabbit scent he had picked up at the base of a large white ash.

Suddenly the heavy double door in the center of the house was thrown wide open and a young man of about twenty-five appeared upon the stone step. His wavy, dark brown hair was drawn back in the fashion of his day and tied with a black ribbon. He wore a brown corduroy coat, buff knee breeches, a long buff waistcoat and riding boots. His face was smooth shaven and tanned from sun and wind, and he gave the impression of both gravity and vitality. He strode toward the water's edge and seemed to be studying the weather. The hound ran to meet him and received an absent-minded caress, while his master turned to the westward and considered the sky above the great trees of the forest behind his home. Several smaller buildings were visible here among the oaks and, from one of them, a young colored man appeared, carrying a red greatcoat of his master's. In his other hand he held a brush and he started at once to give the coat a most vigorous brushing. George Mason, Fourth, for the young planter by the water's edge was he, called to his servant: "Enos, come here and tell me what the weather will be." With a delighted smile, the young negro ran to join Master and dog.

"It gonna clear, Masta Geoge! It gonna be a lubbly day."

"Now Enos, don't you tell me it's going to clear just because you want to go over to Gunston Hall. We don't want to be stormbound there, even if there is to be a party at Madam Fowke's and a gay evening in her kitchen and you may see a wench you've taken a fancy to over there."

Enos giggled happily and his master continued, this time with quiet authority: "Tell Occoquan Nell to give me breakfast and then go to the stable and tell Yellow Dick I shall want the new mare saddled and to come in for my orders. Now, get along! We'll start as soon as possible." Enos vanished into the kitchen, a separate small house on the left, and George, the dog at his heels, turned in to the main house.

An hour later, we see them embarking from the wharf, known as "the Ferry House" on Occoquan Bay, George Mason, his body servant Enos, and two horses. The horses, well blanketed for the ride across the Potomac, stood in the center of the barge. The four rowers, their bodies bent to the task of rowing across the current, were dressed in the blue Mason livery, their heads covered with small velvet caps. George Mason sat, relaxed, in the stern. What thoughts passed through his mind, we can only guess. Probably he thought of the directions he would give his overseer on the Maryland plantation, that part of the estate on which they had lived during his father's life. There was a new tobacco barn to be built, with slatted sides. Here the long leaves would be hung, shielded from the sun but not from the air. It must be started now to be ready for the harvested tobacco in the coming season. Perhaps his mind leaped ahead to the anticipated overnight stay with his cousins, the Fowkes, at their place, named for Gunston Hall in England. Perhaps he considered stopping at Mattawoman, the plantation of Colonel William Eilbeck. It would be interesting to know what Colonel Eilbeck thought of Henry Fielding's new book, *Tom Jones.* Everyone was talking about it and Mr. Eilbeck's comments were always interesting. They were out on the river now. Sails were run up and the rowers relaxed in their places.

George had installed his Maryland overseer in the house where he had lived as a boy, before his father's early death. It was twenty miles downstream. On his arrival, a ride over the plantation and a walk with this man, followed by a visit to one of the negroes who was down with the "bloody flux", finished his business for the day.

Then, accompanied by Enos, George set his face toward the next plantation, Mattawoman, and the Eilbecks. Araby was a hospitable house, part brick, part clapboard, much larger than his small home on Dogue's Neck. Built on high ground, it commanded a wide water view. Mrs. Eilbeck gave him a warm welcome and insisted that he must stay to dine with them at three. It was already after two and her husband and their sixteen year old daughter, Ann would return shortly. They had ridden, she said, to Mr. Smallwood's place,[22] "Smallwood's Retreat," where Mattawoman Creek joined the Potomac, with some of Venus' famous oyster soup. Mrs. Smallwood was ill again.

Barely had she finished speaking when the sound of hoofs was heard, and a moment later, a beautiful girl appeared in the doorway. She was tall and slender, with auburn hair and cheeks rosy with exercise and health. Her black eyes, under beautifully arched brows, were large and kind, though there was a suspicion of coquetry in the long lashes which were lowered as soon as she saw the young man with her mother. Her red riding cloak was about her shoulders but, as she dropped a courtesy, the hood fell from her curls showing a rumpled but proud little head. Mrs. Eilbeck smiled gravely at her daughter's surprise and, to cover the girl's confusion, she bade her go and prepare for dinner.

Ann was replaced in the doorway by the portly form of Colonel Eilbeck. His pleasure at finding their guest was hearty and genuine.

George Mason, however, was momentarily speechless. Why had he never before realized Miss Ann's beauty? Her black eyes had bewitched him and he could only wait for her return. At last she reappeared, descending the graceful stair in the stairhall, directly in George's line of vision. George, standing with her parents at the door of Mr. Eilbeck's study, was apparently listening intently to the older gentleman's account of a new colt he had bought, sired by the famous Janus,[23] but when Ann appeared, our young planter could no longer pretend. He stood gazing up at her like a man in a dream. Mr. and Mrs. Eilbeck exchanged glances as he went to meet her, and at dinner both forebore to comment on his lack of appetite.

"We are going to your cousins' for a ball," Ann announced, over the wild turkey breasts, ham and hushpuppies. "Will you be there, too?"

"If you are going I will be there, too," George replied, wisely including Mrs. Eilbeck with his glance as he spoke. "May I escort you?"

Afternoon found them on their way across the peninsula of southern Maryland to Gunston Hall near Port Tobacco. Mrs. Eilbeck and Ann rode in the chariot with a postillion on one of their horses, and Mr. Eilbeck, George, and a young man named Fanshaw who, much to George's annoyance, had appeared after dinner, accompanied them on horseback. Enos, on a black horse, brought up the rear with one or two of the Eilbeck negroes.

This young Fanshaw was not a stranger to George, but the acquaintance was not a happy one. Peregrin Fanshaw's mother had, as her personal maid, a young negress named Libby. She was a pretty, gentle little creature with clever, deft fingers. She possessed, to the rare degree sometimes found in her race, the ability to make anything grow. Mrs. Fanshaw found her as indispensable in the herb garden as in the sewing room. George Mason's Enos had picked her for the one woman in his world and George had tried to buy her. Mrs. Fanshaw had refused to let her go at any price. The bad part of it was that Libby was treated by the sadistic old Mrs. Fanshaw with out and out

brutality. Enos, who had gone to the Fanshaws' to see Libby
during the dinner hour at Mattawoman, had returned to his
master with fresh tales of cruelty on the Fanshaw plantation,
and the report that one of Libby's smooth brown cheeks was cut
and swollen from a blow from a candle mold in the hand of
her angry mistress.

George turned all this over in his mind as he rode beside the
unwieldly coach which rolled and bounced over the frozen, rutty
road. A chill wind from the Potomac whipped at George's red
greatcoat and Mr. Eilbeck's green one, but it deepened the roses
in Ann's cheeks and roughened the shining coats of the superb
horses. The road lay through a forest of oak, ash, holly and
laurel under a white, translucent, winter sky. Sometimes George
achieved riding at Ann's side, then the road would narrow into
a defile and, when it widened, young Fanshaw would edge in
ahead of him and ride triumphant until another obstacle forced
him back to be replaced by George. Both must, perforce, show
the lady's father every courtesy and ride with him whenever
civility demanded. The hot Fowke blood in George's veins began
to be troublesome, and, by the time the tall twin chimneys of
Gunston Hall appeared above the treetops, George felt he had
not, in all his life, disliked anyone as cordially as Fanshaw.

"Gunston Hall" of the Fowkes was a small, pink, story-and-a-
half brick house conforming to the usual graceful lines of its
day.[24] It stood overlooking the long reach of Nanjemoy Creek
where it flows into the Potomac. With its dependencies, smoke
house, carriage house, spinning house and quarters gathered
about it, Gunston Hall suggested a hen with her brood. The
house bore little resemblance to the ancient farm house in England from which it drew its name.

Within, however, the hospitality, cheer and grace were equal
to any to be found in the Mother Country. The widowed Madam
Fowke, whose prematurely white hair and youthful complexion
made her appear to have powdered her hair, received her guests
with her eldest son at her side. He was a boy of sixteen or
seventeen, an unmistakable Fowke, with all the family charac-

teristics, dark, haughty and strongly built, with his father's and grandfather's straight nose and piercing blue eyes. His preference for his pretty cousin, little Elizabeth Dinwiddie, was strongly marked this evening. With her he danced minuet, jig, and country dance and, although they were so young, the guests whispered behind fans that that would soon be a match.

George's attentions to the beautiful Ann Eilbeck were noted, too. Her demure charm had marked her early for a belle, and tonight it was young George Mason who danced the minuet with her and inspired her lovely smile. As a couple, they held all eyes, and when Ann made her deep courtesy and George his courtly bow, two gossiping old dames, in a deep window seat, whispered that, with their combined fortunes, there would be another great family on the Potomac.

"But my dear Letty," said one old lady, "young Mason won't look at a girl. All the prettiest girls on the Rappahannock and Potomac, as well as in Annapolis, have set their caps for him and he is politely unaware of them."

"Well, my dear Selina," said her friend, "if you don't believe me, look at him this minute!"

George was looking down at his charming partner with his heart in his eyes for all the world to see.

What the world could not hear, however, were his whispered words.

"I will love you always. Will you marry me, Ann?"

Nor could the gossips read Ann's lips. "I think perhaps—someday."

Soon he drew her aside, an intrigue in which Ann proved helpful. A pink bow on her pannier was becoming detached. In Madam Fowke's bedroom, little Libby, there to attend Mrs. Fanshaw, quickly adjusted the slipping bow and when Ann rejoined George, in the momentarily empty dining room, her face was shocked and serious. If they spoke, not of their own love but of the love of Enos and Libby, they were only true to their day and age. A cruel mistress such as Mrs. Fanshaw was the exception, and responsible, affectionate slave owners, who never used the word "slave" and loved "their people", were the general rule.

They discussed Libby's swollen face and Enos' devotion to George, equalled by George's love for Enos. George recounted the story of how Enos had saved his life when they were small boys and had gone after a water moccasin at Mr. John Mercer's on Marlborough Neck. Now Enos was in trouble and Ann could see that George was miserable too. Her black velvet eyes filled with tears and, as young Fanshaw came to seek her out, she gave George such a reassuring smile that his heart seemed to bound from his silver buckled shoes to the stars.

Hours later when the guests had gone, except those who were remaining for the night, George, sleeping in the schoolhouse with the Fowke boys, dreamed of a pair of black velvet eyes, of an unmanageable auburn curl, and of a pink bow on a lady's flowered pannier.

4

As the winter days grew longer, young Mason's interest in the tobacco warehouse being built upon his Maryland plantation, increased steadily. His overseer must have wondered at the frequency of the young owner's visits. His trips across the river always included a stop at the house on Mattawoman Creek.

On one such occasion, he found Mr. and Mrs. Lawrence Washington from Mount Vernon dining with the Eilbecks, for he, as well as Mason, owned land on the Maryland side of the Potomac. Lawrence Washington was a frail young man, and appeared even more so when compared with his eighteen-year-old half-brother George, who accompanied him. Young George Washington towered over his charming but emaciated older brother. He was entirely unconscious of his own good looks. In the presence of the beautiful Ann, he was awkward and shy to the point of taciturnity. Mrs. Eilbeck, presiding with ease at the head of her dinner table, tried kindly to draw him into the conversation. She asked about his recent commission by the College of William and Mary as public surveyor for Fairfax County, and of his earlier trip west as assistant surveyor to Lord Fairfax. George Mason was genuinely interested in all this, for he had a deep concern for his land, and the correct method of making a survey was of importance to him. George Washington was, at last, lured from self-consciousness, and when the Ohio Company, organized the preceding year, became the subject of debate, the conversational ball passed back and forth so quickly that all shyness on young Washington's part was forgotten in the general interest. Both Lawrence Washington and George Mason were members of the Company. Lawrence Washington had, in fact, succeeded old Mr. Thomas Lee as president of the Council and both he and George Mason were keenly aware of the necessity of knowing more of that vast hinterland which lay, green and beckoning, beyond the Virginia mountains. The Ohio Company had for its object the colonization of this western territory and the promotion of trade with the Indians on the Ohio River. There were twenty shareholders with a grant of 600,000 acres and a wealthy London merchant for their agent in England. They had sent out Christopher Gist, the first white settler west of the Allegheny Mountains, to act as their agent there. George Mason's boyhood guardian, John Mercer of Marlborough, was secretary of the company, and Mason had been transmitting supplies for the settlers, of whom there were eleven families with Gist. The peace treaty, signed by England and France in 1748, had not settled the disputed boundary question, and three years after this evening at Colonel Eilbeck's, young George Washington would be sent by Governor Dinwiddie to confer with the French commandant on the Ohio.

Interested as George Mason was in the engrossing problems of the Ohio, he was, nevertheless, constantly aware of Ann's lovely presence. How daintily she ate her partridge, and was there so engaging a curl as the one that curved around her slim white neck? To a casual observer, Mason himself would have presented the appearance of a distinguished young planter intent upon public problems, but Ann knew full well that he was conscious of her every motion. She was not surprised, therefore, when her handkerchief fluttered to the floor, that George Mason retrieved it instantly and replaced it in her hand. She was surprised that young Washington sprang from his chair, too late to perform the same service.

A sixth sense had already warned Mason that he had a rival in this eighteen-year-old youth. Perhaps love had sharpened his perceptions but he had surprised a look in George Washington's keen blue eyes that was unmistakable, and he was alert and on guard. George Washington might be young and awkward and, unlike himself, no heir to a great fortune, but there was something about this boy, seven years his junior, which was arresting and winning. If he set his heart upon a girl he would constitute a dangerous threat to other suitors. As Mrs. Eilbeck rose from the table, and Ann and Mrs. Lawrence Washington followed her into her drawing room, George Mason noticed that Ann looked up at the young giant who had stepped back to let her pass. She smiled and blushed and Washington bowed with an air of distinction which would no doubt increase with maturity.

In the little paneled room to which the gentlemen withdrew, both young men were impatient and bored. Colonel Eilbeck had turned the conversation to horseflesh and he now embarked upon a long story. At last, however, it was finished and he rose saying, "Shall we join the ladies?" "By all means," Lawrence Washington replied, "but I fear we must start for home very shortly."

Mason caught George Washington's look of disappointment. The young man made his home with this older half-brother and his beautiful wife. Everyone knew of the devotion between the brothers and of the anxiety Lawrence's failing health caused the Washington family. Now, in spite of his relief at the three Washingtons' imminent departure, George Mason felt a pang of pity for the younger brother who said promptly and cheerfully, "I will go at once and see that the horses are brought around."

Lovely Mrs. Washington, a sister-in-law of Mrs. Fairfax of Belvoir,[25] was soon mounted; Lawrence and George Washington also, and the little cavalcade vanished to the rhythmical sound of hoofbeats on the frozen road.

Mason made no move to go. Ann had whispered that she had news for him about Libby and he was only too glad of an excuse to stay longer. Bob, one of the houseboys, had just put another

log on the fire in the drawing room and the little group settled
themselves near it, grateful for the warmth. Mrs. Eilbeck chose
a chair behind her tapestry frame. Ann produced some knitting,
and Mr. Eilbeck took up his stand in front of the burning logs.
George picked up a high-backed, straight chair and put it near
Ann for himself. She smiled and said, including her parents,

"George has not heard the Maryland news and I did not want
to speak of death before poor Lawrence Washington, but," turning her great soft eyes to George, "Mrs. Fanshaw died last week.
She became very angry because poor old Romulus served the soup
too hot. Libby says she fell in a fit and never recovered. It
would be wrong to rejoice at anyone's misfortune and I'm sure
that I do not, but a most amazing chain of events has proved
fortunate for Libby. Peregrin Fanshaw has made me a present
of the girl, with strict injunctions that she is never to fall into
your hands."

This last was accompanied by a rosy flush and a downward
sweep of her incomparable lashes.

George bounded from his chair at the good news, exlaiming:
"Ann, Ann, you enchantress! How have you worked this miracle?
How can I thank you? It is too good to be true that Libby is
safe in this happy household!"

In the meantime, a drama no less moving had taken place in
Great Sue's kitchen. Enos, as usual, had accompanied his master.
Great Sue, who ruled Mrs. Eilbeck's kitchen, might have been
an African Amazon Queen. Indeed, she would have been a queen
wherever her lot was cast. She ruled her kitchen minions with
severity, tempered with compassion, and when she saw Enos'
downcast face, her compassion became uppermost.

"What you doin' lookin' like you lost your last frien', Enos
Mason?" she asked. "Don' you know Great Sue goin' give you
the best thing you ever had in yo' life?"

Whatever may have been Great Sue's plan of surprise, Libby
appeared at that moment in the kitchen door. Seeing Enos, she
started like a fawn. All the grace and dignity of a wood creature
were in her every movement.

Enos had none of the white man's inhibitions in the presence of his beloved, but he had the same inborn dignity that distinguished Libby. Slowly, they approached each other, touched hands reverently and went together from the kitchen.

In the drawing room, where George and Ann were aware only of each other, Mrs. Eilbeck went hurriedly to fetch some tapestry wool. Colonel Eilbeck left the room, unable to think of an excuse. George drew Ann gently into his arms.

From that evening, George Mason's life took on all the glowing colors of happiness. Ann's beauty was a source of increasing wonder to him. He had taken it on faith, as a lover does, that her inward beauty was as great as its outward expression. This was indeed the case and their love grew deeper and greater as the days passed.

Spring came early that year in Maryland and Virginia, and a young man, deeply in love, found his way from Dogue's Neck carpeted with emerald green and with spring flowers. The wood road from the highway to Mount Eilbeck seemed a veritable road to Paradise and the house itself appeared in a cloud of ethereal cherry blossoms. Indeed the cherry trees were so numerous that a tradition grew in later generations, that the trees were the result of cherries eaten by Ann's numerous suitors, who ate cherries and left the pits, while waiting for Ann. In Summer, the garden boasted the only blue rambler rose in Maryland. One day, Ann, holding some of the blossoms of the Spring's first arbutus in her hand, showed them proudly to George who had eyes only for the lovely girl herself.

"Roses and lilies,"[26] he said, "are here—the fairest, not in Maryland, alone, but in all the world".

On the day after George obtained her promise, one of Ann's most determined beaux rode up to Mount Eilbeck. Peregrin Fanshaw bit his loose lower lip when he met Mason in the garden with Ann. He acknowledged his rival's presence with the slightest bow and asked at once if Ann would be his lady in the next tournament. This was a meeting held in open field, in which the horsemen called themselves knights and each tilted for the honor of his lady. The winner had the satisfaction of seeing his lady crowned "Queen of Love and Beauty" at the ball which followed the tournament. It was said that Fanshaw sometimes failed to observe the rules and his abnormally long arms made him a dangerous assailant in the lists. Ann did not wish him to be the first to hear of her engagement, nor did she wish to be his lady at the tournament, but she was too kind to hurt him if she could avoid it. Searching for a way out of her dilemma, she asked when the tournament would take place, while Mason, at her side, wondered why she did not give him an immediate "No."

At that moment, George Washington appeared in the doorway, ran down the steps toward them and saluting the two other men, bent over Ann's extended hand. Then, drawing himself to his full height, which was greater than Peregrin Fanshaw's, he said:

"Mistress Ann, I have come to remind you of your promise to be my lady at the coming tournament next Thursday."

There was no denying the honesty in Washington's level blue gaze. Ann had completely forgotten her promise to go as his lady but she recovered herself quickly, and with a look of well simulated regret to Fanshaw, she said to Washington, "Thank you, sir, it will be a pleasure."

At her words, Fanshaw made an awkward bow and turned on his heel toward the garden gate and his waiting horse. As he did so, he caught the hem of Ann's skirt with his spur and ripped it before Mason, who sprang forward, could stop him.

George Mason muttered something uncomplimentary under his breath and Ann, who feared a duel, intervened quickly.

"It is nothing," she said, "and, Peregrin, I am sorry! You must all forgive me, George Washington, too, for I had quite forgotten my promise. Please be nice—all of you!"

This last, with a quick, mischievous look at George Mason, whose expression of melting forgiveness made her blush.

At the tournament, Washington unhorsed Fanshaw and several others and Ann was crowned Queen of Love and Beauty at the ball. The following night there was a play at Upper Marlborough. The players were of a company which had acted in Williamsburg and were on their way to Philadelphia. The theatre was a tobacco-house[27] fitted up for the purpose.[28] George Mason escorted Mr. and Mrs. Eilbeck and Ann to the play and was agreeably concious of the interest their entry occasioned in that gathering of southern Marylanders.

Colonel Eilbeck had decided that the banns for George and Ann should be read that Sunday in church. The church was near Port Tobacco and, in accordance with church law, the banns must be read three successive Sundays. Now the news was known. George's friends could congratulate the fortunate young planter and Ann's beaux make threats of suicide which would not be carried out.

The wedding day came on the 4th of April, 1750 and the service was performed by the Reverend John Moncure.[30] It was customary in those days in Virginia and Maryland for most girls of wealthy families to be married at home.[31] As Paul Wilstach describes these 18th Century weddings, "Cards and dancing immediately succeed," followed later by "an elegant supper, a cheerful glass and the convivial song." The wedding celebration lasted several days and sometimes would move from one house to another, the wedding party, in one such case, occupying six well filled carriages, "the Bride and Bridegroom leading the van in a new Phaeton."[32]

We may be sure that George Mason and Ann Eilbeck had a conservative though beautiful wedding. Wedding veils were not worn then nor were brides dressed in white. We can only guess at Ann's gown, but we know that a fashionable young lady of that period wore a fawn-colored gown with nosegays of purple, red, yellow and white scattered over it, a pleat at the back fell from her neck and ended in a graceful train. Lace ruffles fell from her elbow sleeves and adorned the front of her waist and this was held in with a row of dainty bows down the front and the flounce and falbalos[34] were of silk, pinked. Her hair was powdered and adorned with pearls.

We do know that, to George Mason, she was the fairest bride who ever gave her hand in marriage. We know too that he continued firm in that belief, not only up to the time of her early death but also until his own, many years later.

After George Mason's death, the following lines were found in his pocket book:

"Sweet were the halcyon hours when o'er my bed
  Peace spread her opiate pinions through the night;
  Love scattered roses gently round my head
  And morning waked me to increased delight;
  Yet every future hour resigned I'd bear
  Oh, could I but forget what once they were!
  But nightly visions only keep alive
  The fond remembrance of her much loved form;
  And waking thoughts tend only to revive
  The wreck of joys o'er which I mourn.
  Alas! what can the honors of the world impart
  To soothe the anguish of a bleeding heart."

5

ONE SPRING DAY two years later found our young planter
and his eighteen-year-old wife an established married pair in the
little house on Dogue's Neck.

Taking advantage of the beautiful May day, Madam Mason
had come by boat from Chappawamsic to consult her elder son
upon the approaching trip to England of his young brother,
Thomson. George was out when she arrived, but Enos had been
sent to fetch him. Ann had settled her mother-in-law comfortably by the window looking toward the river. The land between
the house and the shore was laid out in the usual geometric
garden. Box hedges enclosed beds of flowers, vegetables and
herbs, and the fragrance of mint and thyme came in at the window.

The elder Mrs. Mason, even after years of widowhood, was
still a pretty woman. Her bearing and chiseled profile indicated
both intelligence and breeding. She had used all the means at
her command to give the best available opportunities to her three
children. The boys had had English as well as Scottish tutors
and George's education had been burnished, so to speak, by
study and discussion with his guardian, John Mercer of Marlborough. This gentlemen, "forever disable to practice" as an
attorney by the House of Burgesses, because of his insulting
language in the county court, had therefore been free to instruct
his brilliant young ward as no mere tutor could have done.

George, though living at home, had worked with Mr. Mercer on his "Abridgment" for the laws of Virginia, had studied the British Law and Statutes as applied to the Colony of Virginia. Later, when the House of Burgesses reinstated Mercer on a new commission, George had already been given finer legal training than Mrs. Mason could have hoped to obtain for her son.[35] Now, the good lady planned, with George's generous financial help, to send her eighteen-year-old Thomson "home" to England to study.

In this plan, as in all her little activities, Madam Mason had her daughter-in-law's warm and enthusiastic support. They sat facing each other in the sunny window, their faces alight with interest. Ann knew that it would be a hard wrench for the older woman to let the last of her three children go, for George's exquisite little sister Mary was now Mrs. Selden and living near Fredericksburg. Thomson's departure, dearly as Madam Mason desired it, would leave a great emptiness in the little house at Chappawamsic, and Ann planned to ask her help often in the future. This would not be too difficult with her first baby on the way. There was an exciting bit of news, too, but she would leave that for George to tell his mother when he came.

"Perhaps Thomson will go to Hollin Hall," Ann said, referring to the English home of Madam Mason's own family, the Thomsons.

"Yes," the older woman replied, "I hope so, and I should like him to read law at the Middle Temple in London as my father and grandfather did. But enough about Thomson, and my plans! Tell me, my dear child, how are you feeling? You are pretty as a picture carrying your baby. I wish my little Mary looked as blooming as you!"[38]

Ann assured her that she had never felt better, and at that moment, both women turned expectant faces toward the door, for George's step and voice were heard in the hall, and there he was, ruddy and handsome as ever. His first glance was for Ann and then his arms were around his mother in one of his warm and tender embraces. Over his mother's head George gave Ann a questioning look. She answered with a negative shake of her head.

"Don't tell her till I come back," she said with a mischievous smile and vanished through a door on the other side of the fireplace to give some directions to Occoquan Nell about dinner.

When she returned there was another exchange of glances with her husband, and Madam Mason, who missed nothing, exclaimed:

"Well, tell me what is this secret! George is bursting with some news he refused to share with me till your return. Out with it! My patience is gone!"

George stood up and began to pace back and forth across the room, speaking slowly and thoughtfully as was his habit unless greatly stirred.

"We have a commission in London for Thomson," he said. "You know, Mother, this little house is really too small for our growing family, and we plan to ask Thomson to find in England and bring back to us a capable builder to construct a larger house, one more suited to our needs. I know the type of house I wish but I need better workmanship than I can find here. Under your careful training, Thomson has developed excellent taste. I have perfect confidence in his ability to find a good man and in his tact to persuade him to come to Virginia."

Madam Mason's face had lighted with pleasure at her son's first words and her enthusiasm for the new house almost equaled her children's. Among other questions, she asked.

"What will you name the new house?"

Again George became thoughtful.

"It cannot," he said, "be Hollin Hall; that name is for Thomson, since he has your maiden name. Ann and I have thought of calling our new home Gunston Hall, for in addition to Grandmother's family place in Staffordshire, it was at Gunston Hall in Maryland that I fell in love with my beautiful Ann."

He said this with his arm around Ann's shoulders, drawing her toward him and kissing the top of her head as he spoke.

"That is a beautiful name," Madam Mason agreed, "and your

choice would have given your father great happiness. It pleases me too."

No golden moment was ever uninterrupted in those busy plantation days. At this moment, the most appalling sounds issued from the kitchen, and George, followed by Ann, and Ann by Madam Mason, hurried to the source of the confusion. Through the door beside the chimney, down the steps and across the grass they went to the separate house which was Occoquan Nell's kitchen. Her cries and imprecations resounded, accompanied by the sound of ringing metal.

There stood the enormous Nell, part Indian, part negress, her gorgeous red bandana awry. A great cauldron of hot soup lay spilling its contents on the brick floor before her, while she held by the seat of his trousers her small son, Bob. From his hand dangled the remains of a large dead rattlesnake.

Enos' gentle little Libby, now known as "Liberty" since her release from the Fanshaws, cowered terrified in a corner. It was upon her, as well as on Bob, that Nell now poured denunciations.

The appearance of the Master and Mistress and of Madam Mason, still "Miss Nancy" to Nell, ended all sound, and the Master's quiet voice seemed to bring order and security back to the kitchen.

"Nell, put Bob down. Bob, take that snake out of the kitchen at once. You may keep it," he added, remembering his own snake hunting expeditions with Enos, "but you must never bring it indoors again. Do you understand?"

"Yes Sir," and the boy and snake vanished with unbelievable speed.

The Mistress spoke then. "Liberty, what are you doing behind the work table?" she asked. "Come here. Was Bob frightening you with that snake? Didn't you know it was dead?"

"No, Mis' Mason. I'm 'fraid a snakes, daid or livin'." "An' look," cried Nell, silent till now, "all my good soup on the flo'. What am I goin' give Miss Nancy for her dinner now?"

"Why Nell," cried Madam Mason, "it's such a treat for me

when I come here, to have your cookin' again, I just don't care what you give me. If I didn't have a thing but those good beaten biscuits of yours, I'd be perfectly happy!"

"It's all right, Nell," Ann reassured her. "You and I will plan the best dinner in the world right now. And Liberty, come and help poor Nell clean up this mess, and next time you go over with me to Chappawamsic, you ask Nan Old Gate to tell you about when the Master was a little boy and about the water moccasin skin he and Enos brought home from Marlborough. They had tucked it into a box of fine books from Mr. Mercer's library!"

Slowly peace was restored. Ann remained in the kitchen a little longer, but George and his mother walked slowly through the garden before reentering the house.

"Tell me," Madam Mason asked thoughtfully, "about this little Liberty of Ann's. Is she not the one you told me about whom Mrs. Fanshaw treated so badly? A dreadful woman!"

"Yes," George replied. "Her son, Peregrin, was in love with Ann. He is as bad as his mother, really, but has the wit to hide his cruel nature, and if you don't look too closely at his hard eyes and loose lower lip, you might find his apologetic manner disarming. Ann was sorry for him at first. She thought him the victim of his mother's harshness. He hates me for two reasons: I married Ann; and she brought Liberty into my household."

"You frighten me," his mother began.

"Oh no, no cause for that," George answered. "He cannot hurt me, but he has tried to get Liberty back and I think he would kill her if he could. That is why Ann always keeps her with her. Fanshaw sent a white weaver of his to study, so he said, our methods. He told Liberty, who was in the herb garden, that her mistress was calling and then tried to grab her on her way to the house. He didn't know her husband was around. Enos knocked him down and he went home in a white-hot fury. I had an ugly letter from Fanshaw which I answered with a threat of the law and no more came of it."

From this they drifted into conversation about the slave trade and George spoke bitterly of the greed in England, and in New England too, which fostered a practice which he termed wicked as well as cruel.

"Every master of slaves," he said, "is born a petty tyrant."[37]

"Why George, my dear son," exclaimed gentle Madam Mason, shocked by her son's strong feeling, "Surely you do not think of me as a tyrant with dear Nan Old Gate or my Nell or Beck?"

"No, no, Mother," George replied more gently. "I am sorry to have startled you but we are in grave danger, for what we are doing is wrong. Unless the slave trade is ended there will be a terrible reckoning. It is not enough that we, and others like us, love our people. The system is wrong, and injustice carries its own inevitable punishment."

Then he added, thoughtfully: "Nations, unlike people, cannot be punished in the next world, national punishment comes in this world."[38]

Ann had joined them unobserved and was listening gravely.

"The King could stop it," she said wistfully.

George nodded. "I wonder if his ministers have put it to him clearly," he said.

Madam Mason spoke softly as if to herself, repeating the ancient British rule for brave men:

"Love God. Honor the King and do your part."

"My part?" George questioned.

"To write the King," Ann said. "Dear George, no one can make things as clear as you; write to his Majesty and ask him to help us."

There in the Virginia sunshine, in his quiet garden by the river, it seemed such a simple thing to write the King and set it right. The Occoquan stream on the south of Dogue's Neck sang its little song of small water pouring into a great river as it emptied itself into the Potomac, and George and Ann and George's mother planned together a small message that would lose itself also in a great London bureaucracy. Farther back in Virginia, the Occoquan becomes Bull Run. Here a century later, boys in blue and boys in grey would die for a nation's punishment because a letter failed in its purpose.

Liberty came out of the kitchen to tell Ann that dinner was almost ready. Mistress and maid smiled into each other's eyes with complete understanding and affection. There was no negro problem on Dogue's Neck in the year 1752.

Shortly after Madam Mason's visit, George and Ann rode over to Colonel Blackburn's at Rippon Lodge[39] for dinner and the night. Returning the next day, they turned from the King's Highway into the gate to their own property. The road from there to their plantation on the tip of Dogue's Neck peninsula, lay through woods of oak and beech and through cleared meadows where sheep and cattle grazed. Ann wore a riding habit of green and a large hat of green beaver, the crown encircled with a band of gold which matched the gold of her curls. Her horse, a gift from her father, was a little mare which Colonel Eilbeck had bought from Mr. Tasker. A daughter of the famous mare, Selima,[40] she was of the finest strain of horseflesh in Maryland. Birds sang their love songs overhead and the wood road was gay with wild flowers. Mayapples spread their five-fingered canopies in patches and resembled fairy umbrellas under the trees.[41]

George hummed the old tune, *"My Lady Greensleeves."* Ann joined in the song and soon they were carolling as gaily as the birds.

"I wonder if she married him," Ann said.

"Who married whom?" asked her husband.

"Why, the Lady Greensleeves," Ann replied. "I hope so. He wrote poems for her that were almost as lovely as the ones you write for me."

"I don't know," George replied, "but I'm sure of one thing —she was not so beautiful as my lady! Of that we can be certain."

The little mare interrupted them here by shying prettily and the riders reined in their horses while a mother skunk and her three kittens crossed their path and vanished with unhurried dignity under some laurel bushes.

A few moments later, horses and riders emerged from the woods onto a cleared plateau. Sheep grazed among the hummocks, and directly in front of them, the land fell away sharply. The country at their feet was a primeval forest, still untouched by the woodman's axe. It appeared, like the mystical land of Lyonesse, to be a country which might vanish at any moment beneath the waters of the Potomac which washed its banks on three sides. At the end of the peninsula lay their home plantation. The house, except for its tall chimneys, was hidden from view by tall forest trees.

"Here we are!" George Mason exclaimed. "This is where I always planned to build my house."

He dismounted, and leading his horse and hers, stopped close to the sudden drop in the land. Ann's soft murmurs of pleasure delighted him.

"Do you really like it, honey?" he asked, looking up for her smile. "This would be the garden and the house would be back there," with a wave of his arm toward the north and west. "There is ample room for a large house with dependencies, quarters, stables, smoke house, spinning house, everything. . . . It would be healthier here than where we are, so close to the river. You know, my sweet, that is why Stratford and all the newer houses are built back and on high land. The mosquito made an end of Jamestown, and Williamsburg was found to be healthier. I'm impatient to begin the house here, for I want to take no chances with my family's health."

Ann laughed contentedly at the word "family," for she knew George referred to the baby she was carrying and to others, they hoped, would follow. She looked about her at the lush green meadow, the grazing sheep, the wall of forest trees behind them and at the Potomac, that shining river which was the way back to civilization. One of her friends had married and returned to England, but her home was here. Here she would live out her days, raise George's and her children and be buried at last beside the man she loved.

At that moment, George and Ann Mason might have been the subject of an artist's brush. As it is, however, we can see them only with the mind's eye—Ann sitting her horse, there in the sunny meadow, with her husband standing beside her and his horse cropping the grass at his master's feet. George in red coat and ruffled shirt, booted and spurred, his dark hair in a queue, stood with his face lifted to Ann. His ruddy countenance was alive with interest and devotion. Mistress Mason's superbly tall and slender figure was shown to advantage on a horse and, from the cluster of auburn curls under her broad-brimmed hat to the toe of her small riding boot which protruded from the full green skirt of her habit, George was finding her perfection itself.

"We could have lots of cherry trees," Ann said, "like the ones at Mattawoman. I love cherry blossoms."

"And I love cherries and cherry brandy," George replied, leaning his head against her in a momentary caress.

Then he swung himself lightly into his saddle, and they continued their way across the meadow and back to the wood road which was their way home. It circled the drop in the land and took them lower and lower by easy stages, till they came out of the woods by the landing on the shore. Here stood a tobacco warehouse and some fishermen's shacks. A man mending his nets under a huge live oak gave them his salutation as they passed.

That evening Ann, beautiful in panniered skirt and with lace ruffles at her elbows, sat before her spinnet, while George turned the pages of music by Scarlotti, Bach and Rameau. At last Ann's slender fingers felt for the notes of "My Lady Greensleeves" and they sang again the wistful air, snuffed out the candles on the spinnet, and lighted only by the moon, went into the adjoining room which was their chamber.

6

O<small>N</small> THE North American continent, the mid-eighteenth century brought vicious boundary disputes between England and France. Here, they were called the French and Indian War; in Europe, their repercussion was the Seven Years' War. The borders of Virginia were often under attack and the sultry threat of coming trouble hung heavy in the air.

At Dogue's Neck, however, the peace of a well run plantation seemed to deny all unpleasant possibilities. The house, which was only a dream in 1752, was now, in 1759, entirely finished and had begun to lose its look of newness. Standing high upon a bluff on Dogue's Neck, Gunston Hall was a brick house, a story and a half high and of an architecture known later as mid-Georgian. It was more of a cottage than a manor, though the large number of small houses clustered about it gave it the appearance of a small community, as indeed it was.

Here, one May evening when the setting sun threw long shadows across the grass, a man of about twenty-five stepped briskly out of the small house on the right, and with a graceful, easy stride went up the steps to the porch on the land front of the new house. He was tall and slim with a finely moulded, sensitive face,[42] a well proportioned build, and hands which denoted as much fineness of nature as his features. This was William Buckland, until recently, indentured servant to George Mason, and London craftsman whom Thomson Mason had brought back from London to his brother as architect for the new Gunston Hall. When a boy of fourteen, he had been apprenticed to his uncle, a joiner and bookseller of London. With what uncertainty he had set sail from England four years before carrying with him his few possessions.[43] These included his precious books, given him by his Uncle James,[44] damaged copies, to be sure, from the shelves of his London book stall, but a priceless heritage to a young man whose ambition was to follow in the footsteps of the great master craftsmen, William Kent, Abraham Swan, Palladio, Vitruvius, Chippendale, and many others. His books stood now upon the shelf he had fashioned for them in his room in the dependency. The little house where he lived was to be a schoolhouse for the two boys still in the nursery and for others yet to come. His chamber would become the tutor's. But never would such intensive study take place there as young Buckland had put into this, his first architectural assignment.

As a small boy in Oxfordshire, William had watched, enchanted, when Honington Hall was altered.[45] Then had followed seven years with his uncle in London, studying the Books in the shop and working earnestly under the supervision of some of London's greatest joiners and cabinet workers. Then, but he would not remember the heartbreak of a broken romance. When his uncle had taken him to the Inner Temple and he had met Thomson Mason he had gladly accepted the American gentleman's offer of passage to the new world. Now again his world was rosy with hope. The years of his indenture were over and Mr. Mason had endorsed his paper stating that he, Buckland, had done all the joining and carving in the house. Furthermore, Mr. Mason had recommended him to friends in nearby Dumfries and had spoken of a possibility of employing him on the new Glebe House in Truro Parish.[46] Besides all this there was a little maid named Mary Moore.[47] On the porch William Buckland paused. His memory flashed back to Oxford and to the parish of St. Peter-in-the-East where he had been born.

Even after four years he had occasional twinges of homesickness for England. Men spoke of England as the parent country and Mr. Mason had said at dinner:

"We are constantly being reprimanded in the authoritative style of a master to a schoolboy."[48]

"Well, it is a wonderful country," Buckland mused. "I have thrown in my lot here, and here I shall remain."

Stepping into the wide center hall the young architect was arrested by the sound of children's high-pitched voices—punctuated from time to time by the sweet notes of Mrs. Mason's soft speech and the rich notes of Old Beck. Then a childish monotone indicated that, in Mrs. Mason's room, little George and Nancy were saying their prayers at their mother's knee—two at a time was the rule and Beck was having difficulty in restraining William, the youngest, who wished to join in. "I want to say, 'God bless Enos—now'," he wept.

Walking softly not to disturb them, Buckland turned in to the Palladian room on the right. This was his favorite room. He was glad that he had designed the niches higher and narrower than his books of directions indicated. Their proportions pleased him for they gave height and dignity to the little parlor. He moved to one of the two windows looking toward the river . . . for in Virginia this side of the house was known as the river front to distinguish it from the land front, approached from the road.

Here before him lay the tiny box hedges laid out in geometric designs on each side of a broad allée, which was also outlined with box. At the foot of the garden the land fell away sharply to a lower terrace and then to the low peninsula of Dogue's Neck. There, far below on the edge of the Occoquan river, lay Old Plantation[49] where the second Mason had lived.

A low cough startled him and he was embarrassed to discover that he was not alone. That tiresome little Sarah Brent had been there all along. She was so small, so colorless, and so quiet in all her birdlike motions that Buckland felt she was constantly seeing and hearing things not intended for her eyes or ears. The unmarried sister of Mrs. Graham who lived in nearby Dumfries, Sarah was a frequent visitor. Perhaps Mrs. Mason liked her, perhaps she pitied her; certainly Sarah, or Sally as they all called her, was a welcome visitor. Buckland had the uncomfortable suspicion that if he were to seat himself beside her and take her hand she would not draw it away. There was a pause and then Sally said sweetly:

"I didn't wish to startle you for you seemed so intent on your own thoughts. You know of course how pleased Mr. and Mrs. Mason are with your work?"

There seemed no suitable reply to this, so Buckland remained silent and Sally ran on—"Have you heard what happened at the Truro vestry meeting today? No?" As Buckland shook his head —"You know how dissatisfied the Reverend Mr. Green has been for ages with that good-for-nothing Waite. He has put such poor brick into the walls of the Glebe House that it is ready to fall, though not completed, and you, Mr. William Buckland—are to be given the task of rebuilding it! You are the coming architect of Virginia and little Sally Brent congratulates you."

At her words, Buckland, always quick and purposeful in movement, had fairly dashed to the chair near her.

"Oh Miss Sally, you can't mean what you say! You are not teasing me! It would be cruel."

At that moment he almost thought her pretty. She was a nice girl after all.

"Tell me, how do you know all this?" he asked.

It was true that Sally was small and colorless and without great charm, but she was of the family of that doughty old fighter Captain Giles Brent who had fought at Kent Island, and later, with Colonel Gerard Fowke, Mr. John Lord and Captain George Mason, had affronted the king of the Potawomack Indians, and still later, with Captain Mason, had fired on the Doegs and so helped to touch off Bacon's Rebellion.

Now, Sally was past the marrying age and unmarried, and was becoming desperate. She wanted a home and children. She knew that young Buckland was marked for greatness—and beyond all this, she had fallen in love with him. His handsome, aware face, sensitive hands and lithe, graceful figure enchanted her. She owned a little land, a few negroes. He could build a house . . .

She smiled and made a place for him on the bench beside her.

Just then the racket arose which always accompanied Mr. Mason's arrival. Old Orion, the ancient foxhound, now very decrepit, preceded his Master into the room and stretched himself before the empty fireplace. He made a great circumstance of the act of lying down.

"Well Sally, have you been telling Buckland the good news?" Mason asked.

"I was about to tell him," Sally said, blushing. "I hope you don't mind. I thought it was too good to keep."

Mason brushed aside her embarrassment.

"Quite right," he said, and then repeated what Sally had already told.

Then, raising his voice he called:

"Ben, bring in the persimmon brandy"—and to Buckland— "we'll drink to the success of all your future building." Ben appeared with a silver salver and glasses and placed the mahogany decanter holder near his master. Mr. Mason poured out the brandy and giving a glassful to Buckland filled another for himself.

"May you fill the Colony of Virginia," he said, "with the beauty of your thoughts expressed in wood and stone!"

Buckland thanked him with a graceful little bow, and then raising his glass a second time he said:

"And to you sir and Mrs. Mason, and may this new country of yours be as fine as you deserve for your children and children's children!"

Just then Mrs. Mason appeared, dainty and charming, in a gown of blue gauze. She congratulated Buckland on his appointment:

"We all know what you can do," she said, "And we hope you will continue to live here as long as you want to."

Sally Brent had again become very quiet and Mrs. Mason looked at her once or twice with a faintly puzzled expression.

Sally, feeling her curious glance, pulled herself together and said, "Was Colonel Washington at the vestry meeting today?"

"No, he was not there," Mason replied. "His bride has come down with measles. He is quite anxious about her and sent word that he would not be present."

Mrs. Mason was deeply sympathetic. All had been greatly interested in the romance of their distinguished neighbor, Ann's one-time, inarticulate lover, who had referred to her as the "Low-land Maid".[50]

During the past weeks Mount Vernon had undergone much polishing and furbishing in preparation for its new mistress, and Colonel Washington had brought the little Widow Custis, now Mrs. Washington, to her new home. The Masons had been among the first to call and had liked the little lady instantly, as indeed everyone did, for it was impossible not to like one so friendly, cheerful and considerate of others.

Later that evening in their own room, Ann in her ruffled white nightgown sat before her swell-front chest of drawers and Chippendale looking glass. As she brushed out her silky auburn curls and recurled them for the night, George stood marvelling at the play of candlelight on his wife's golden head.

Outside in the moonlight, the whippoorwill called wistfully, and occasionally the sound of the negroes' melodious voices floated to them from the quarters beyond the kitchen.

The last curl made, George leaned down and took her in his arms.

"On such a night," he said, "Leander swam the Hellespont, but I have all my heart's treasure here in my arms."

Upstairs, in the guest room which overlooked the moonlit garden, Sarah Brent wept into her pillow. She had heard the hoofbeats of Buckland's horse and knew he had ridden up the "Gravelly Road"[51] to see his Mary, that little Virginia flower in whom centered all his dreams of a new life in a new world.

The Masons Visit the Washingtons

7

Happy years appear to pass more rapidly than sad ones, and for thirteen more happy summers Gunston Hall lay in the sun, growing more mellow and gracious with each year. The garden's geometric form took on cool, green beauty. The avenue of blackheart cherry trees filled Mason with especial pride and pleasure. This avenue began about two hundred feet from the northern, or land front of the Hall, and, from the door of the house, there appeared to be only four beautifully trained and clipped trees. Actually, however, there were many, trees, two rows on each side of the drive, for about 1200 feet. The carriageway was in the center, and a footpath on either side, between the rows of trees, led to the "White Gate." From the "White Gate" to the "Rid Gate," which opened on the King's highway, a hedge of English hawthorn bordered the drive. In the fields the grain and tobacco crops throve. Grain was for home use and tobacco for export. Brandy was distilled from apples, persimmons and peaches, but the grain was kept for food. There were cattle for dairy products and hides. A valuable stallion lived in regal isolation in his meadow and in the stables, which were hidden by the great trees behind the schoolhouse, mares foaled, and charming little thoroughbred colts grew up and were broken, ridden and loved. There were four plantations on the Mason lands of Dogue's Neck. Each consisted of four or five hundred acres under an overseer. A new path was beaten east of the house, running through the kitchen enclosure, past the servants' quarters and through woods, pastures and fields to the river landing for large boats, and here small boats for fishing and hunting were tied up, too.

Within the great house the years, by 1765, had brought six children. George, the eldest, was 12, Ann, called Nancy, was 10 and as beautiful and serene of spirit as her mother. Next came two little boys, William and Thomson, eight and six; the Poppets, the family called them. In that year, the babies were two little girls, mischievous Sally of five years and angelic little Mary.

There had been winters at Gunston Hall, too; winters of the soul as well as of the season: George's beautiful sister Mary Selden had died, leaving two small children; Ann had lost her father, the hearty and kind Colonel Eilbeck, and last of all, George's mother had recently gone, leaving the Mason family enriched by the memory of a really great lady. Nine of her negroes had come to live in the quarters beyond the kitchen. Among them was Nan Old Gate; her pleasant, light-brown face shining with good will for everyone, but especially for little Mary who, when missing, could always be found sitting on Aunt Nan's doorstep drinking in tales of "sperets, hants and teches." Little Mary loved to hear the one of the spirit Aunt Nan had seen in the grain field. She had warned old master to harvest the grain, but the field hands, busy with tobacco harvesting, had waited. That night a fearful storm had laid low the grain and ruined the crop. Next morning, as the sun rose, old Nan had heard the "speret" laugh as it vanished over the marsh on a wild turkey.

For Mr. and Mrs. Mason the years were full of contentment. Their arduous tasks as Master and Mistress of a great plantation were performed in a setting of peace and great beauty. George Mason had no steward for his vast estate of between four and five thousand acres. He superintended the work of his carpenters, coopers, sawyers, blacksmiths, tanners, curriers, shoemakers and distillers, as well as the "hands" who worked in tobacco and grain fields and orchards. His exquisite Ann was as busy as any great lady chatelaine of a medieval castle. The spinning, weaving and knitting for the many dependents of the plantation was done under her direction. In addition, she supervised the cooking, the curing of the hams and the making of jellies and pickles. These last were stored in the cupboard to the left of the fireplace in her room. In addition to these activities, there were the many human problems: a sick negro, a new baby, a prescription to be compounded for the prevalent bloody flux. George and Ann went about the work with at least one son or daughter always near; learning, from watching their parents, the skills they would someday practice on their own plantations. But it was a good life, and George Mason found it very good. "Prefer," he said to his boys, "the happiness and independence of a private station to the troubles and vexations of Public Business."[52]

His years of "happiness and independence," however, were drawing to a close. Relentlessly, inexorably, in the centuries behind him, there had been growing in the soul of man the knowledge of a greath truth. It had started nearly eighteen centuries before. Ineradicable words had been spoken by One who had valued human personality. The value of the individual man or woman had come to stay. Vaguely humanity had grasped the great Fact. In Britain, the new idea had taken firm root. To be sure, it had grown throughout Christendom, but its progress had been faster and surer in Britain. Possibly this was because so many races had produced a people equipped to understand that each race and each person is of value. When the dispossessed Saxon thane asserted his freedom from the Norman lord, perhaps he remembered the Celtic peoples, who had asserted their rights under Saxon overlords.

George Mason was not unfamiliar with Britain's progress, and John Mercer had schooled him well in the history of English Common Law. This knowledge had been put into daily practice on the plantation he owned, in the county where he was His Majesty's Justice, and in the church where he served as vestry-

man of Truro Parish. As the fateful years wore on, this son of
England would remain staunch and true to the truth he had
been taught.

See him, then, on the 6th day of June in this year of 1766. It
had been a long and busy day, beginning at sunrise, when he had
been summoned to the stable to give his wise and careful attention to a sick horse. There had been a bill of lading to make out
for a shipment of tobacco to Glasgow. Two negroes had had a
quarrel over a girl. One had been badly cut, and he had had to
bandage the wound with his own hands. The head carpenter
had run out of glue and he had been forced to send to Colonel
Washington, at Mount Vernon, to borrow eight pounds.[53] Now
it was evening; he could hear the low tones of Ann's and
Nancy's voices as they stitched by candlelight in the parlor across
the hall. He would like to have joined them. He wanted to ask
Ann if she thought Sally Brent were really going to marry that
despicable Fanshaw after all. Poor girl, she wanted a home, and
he had been after her for years. But there would be no happiness for her in such a match. He must try to remember to suggest to Ann that she try to dissuade her from such foolishness.
An unmarried woman in her middle years often fell prey to the
most undesirable man in the community. Young Buckland had
certainly eluded her charm, but he was much too young, and
with all his ability, she was far more clever than he. He had
married that pretty child, Mary Moore, instead, and now they
had moved to Annapolis.

With a sigh he moved the candlestand nearer his small, nut-
wood writing table and took out the almost finished letter to the
Committee of Merchants in London. A packet was to sail the
following evening and he wished to send his letter to the *Public
Ledger* for publication in London. He scanned what he had
written:[54]

"Virginia, Potomac River. "There is a letter of yours dated
the 23rd of February last, lately published in the public papers
here.

"I shall . . . invoke the rights of a Freeman in making such
remarks upon it as I think proper.

"The epithets of parent and child have been so long applied to Great Britain and her colonies that individuals have adopted them, and we rarely see anything from your side of the water free from the authoritative style of a master to a school-boy. . . . Is not this a little ridiculous when applied to the millions of as loyal and useful subjects as any in the British Dominion who have been only contending for their birthrights?"

Then, further down, he reread carefully:

"It is by invitations and indulgence, and not by compulsion, that the market for British manufactures is to be kept up and increased in America. . . . There is a passion natural to the mind of man, especially a free man, which renders him impatient of restraint. Do you—does any sensible man—think that three or four millions of people, not naturally defective in genius, or in courage, who have tasted the sweets of liberty in a country that doubles its inhabitants every 20 years; in a country abounding in such variety of soil and climate—capable of producing not only the necessaries but the convenience and delicacies of life—will long submit to oppression; if, unhappily, for yourselves, oppression should be offered them? Such another experiment as the stamp-act would produce a general revolt in America!"

He took up his quill pen and continued:

"These are the sentiments," he wrote, "of a man who spends most of his time in retirement, and has seldom meddled in public affairs. . . ."

So wrote a man whom Jefferson, years later, was to characterize as "the pen of the Revolution."

Ann entered softly. She had sent Nancy upstairs to bed, and she knew that her husband was very weary. She moved nearer and read over his shoulder as he wrote, continuing to describe himself:

"An Englishman in his principles; a zealous asserter of the Act of Settlement, firmly attached to the present royal family upon the throne; unalienably affected to His Majesty's sacred person and government, in defense of which he would shed the last drop of his blood."

Ann looked lovingly down at him as he continued—he was

often ill, now. The doctors diagnosed it as "convulsive cholic, complicated by gout in his stomach." As he continued to write, "They are the principles of more than nine-tenths of the people who have been so basely misrepresented to you." She said, "Come, George, it is already late, and you must rest."

The letter was soon finished and sealed with his father's signet ring and placed upon a silver salver on the hall table. In the morning Enos would take it, with other mail for England, down to a small boat at the foot of the new path. He would sail over to Dumfries and deliver it there into the hands of the captain of the vessel sailing for London.

But George could not sleep. Ann—her eyes closing with weariness—forced herself to walk with him in the garden. Back and forth they paced together in the soft June evening. It was not of the plantation or of the children, or of their friends that he wanted to talk.

"True," he said, "the stamp act has been repealed, but that is not the end. They do not understand, in England, the line of thought that men are taking here. I was brought up on: 'Honor all men, serve God, follow the King.'"

"First Peter—2nd chapter," Ann said, "but there is more."

"I know," George replied quickly. But it is that part, 'follow the King.' We may find ourselves as Israel did—under a cruel king when the cry went up, 'To thy tents, O Israel!' I don't know that I ever told you of a kinsman of my grandfather, down in Accomac County on the Eastern Shore. Edmund Scarborough was his name. Like my great-grandfather, they were all cavaliers, loyal to the king, and in England Cromwell was in power. The Puritan governor called the Burgesses together here in Virginia, but no one was called from Royalist Accomac. Scarborough called the Accomac planters together and they drew up the Northampton protest. 'No taxation', they said in effect 'without representation'. Scarborough[53a] was always in trouble, and always managed to land on his feet. He might have lost his head, but Cromwell died and it all blew over. The Stuart Kings and Cromwell learned, to their sorrow, that Englishmen cannot be enslaved."

With a clairvoyance of which he was unaware, he added, "I shudder when I think of the future, for it appears inevitable that those events which have happened before are about to be repeated, with the result that a new and great nation will emerge—freed from the ties to the Crown."

Ann put her hand in her husband's and whispered, "Please, God, may this not come true!"

8

THE MONTHS and years that followed George and Ann Mason's midnight walk in the garden at Gunston Hall bore vivid testimony to his accuracy as a prophet. The repeal in England of the Stamp Act was quickly followed by a declaration that the King, with consent of Parliament, had authority to make laws to bind the colonies in all respects. The Townsend Acts followed imposing further duties and a Boston town meeting adopted a non-importation agreement. Virginia followed with a similar resolution. Mrs. Mason, in company with all her neighbors, refused to wear gowns imported from England and dressed her household and herself in homespun woven on the plantation, and conversation on all occasions swung back and forth over the disturbances. In Massachusetts the General Court had drawn up a petition to the King and sent a circular letter to the other colonies, and British troops arriving in Boston had been refused quarters. Ann joined the Daughters of Liberty, as did all the other ladies of the surrounding plantations, Mrs. Washington at Mt. Vernon, Mrs. McCarty at Cedar Grove, Mrs. Cockburn[56] at nearby Springfield, and many more. Sally Fairfax at Belvoir, the next peninsula above Doeg's Neck, remained staunchly Tory and was quiet and unlike her usual lively self these days. Sarah Brent, staying with her pretty sister Jane, Mrs. Richard Graham, in nearby Dumfries, was also very thoughtful under the influence of their sister who had married into the powerful Douglas clan of Scotland. Feeling ran very high among the ladies, as among the men, and Ann's gentle tact saved many an awkward situation. The slowly rising crescendo of public indignation, however, did not prevent the attendance of many of these ladies at the Queen's birthnight ball in Williamsburg at the Governor's Palace. Nor did it prevent the drinking of Their Majesties' health, for were they not all Englishmen and women and loyal subjects of the House of Hanover? A century before, William of Orange had started these Hanoverian Kings upon a jurisdiction acceptable to Englishmen at home and abroad. He had then signed a Bill of Rights written by Somers. To be sure, it left the power of the Crown unimpaired and the authority of Parliament beyond any definite control of the people, although, as George Mason would later say in his Fairfax Resolves, ". . . the most important and valuable part of the British Constitution, upon which its very existence depends, is the fundamental principle of the People's being governed by no laws to which they have not given their consent by representatives freely chosen by the laws they enact equally with their constituents, to whom they are accountable, and whose burdens they share, in which consist the safety and happiness of the community . . ."

Safe in their faith in the country from which their forebears had come, the Washingtons, the Masons and all the planters gathered in Williamsburg that night and celebrated the Queen's birthnight as their fathers had done before them. It was almost a week's trip by carriage from Gunston Hall to Williamsburg. Mr. and Mrs. Mason had brought three of their children with them. Young George was now a handsome boy of 16, Nancy was 14, "the poppets," William and Thomson, had been left at home as punishment for schoolboy deviltry and insubordination to a new tutor, but the irrespressible Sally, aged nine, had been brought along, more to simplify the household they left than because her lively presence would be an addition to the trip to Williamsburg. Eight of the nine Mason children had now arrived. The last, Thomas, would put in his appearance in the following year and his sex and personality were already matters of as much interest to his parents as had been George Junior's, seventeen years before.

This was a thrilling moment for Nancy, her first real ball, and it was upon her account that Mrs. Mason had made the effort to attend. Much time and thought had been spent upon her gown in order not to use imported stuff. Ann Mason had had a gown that had belonged to George's mother made over for this good and beautiful little granddaughter, now almost fifteen. The pale green brocade set off Nancy's auburn curls, exactly the color her mother's had been when she was sixteen and George had lost his heart to her. Nancy's rose leaf skin needed no touch of powder and Mrs. Mason, who disliked any ostentation or pretense, looked at her daughter's natural beauty with pardonable pride. Sally, her yellow curls bobbing, danced around her sister with exclamations of delight and envy.

The Masons were guests of Mr. George Wythe[57]—one of the few permanent residents of Williamsburg. His house fronted directly upon the Palace Green, and was therefore within a few steps of the Palace. The brick house with its wide center hall, graceful stair and well proportioned rooms, was, as was Gunston Hall, the center of its own small community. Mrs. Wythe's graciousness and Mr. Wythe's courtly charm made them welcome. It was a golden moment for all, both young and old, and they partook of the spirit of the moment with enthusiasm. Mrs. Wythe admired Mrs. Mason's gown and beauty, and Mr. Wythe, discussing world problems with Mr. Mason, interrupted their talk over a glass of peach brandy, to toast a new beauty in Virginia, Miss Nancy, and also a future belle, Miss Sally. While the ladies and gentlemen were preparing for the ball, there was activity in the stable and coach house and soon the Wythe coach appeared at the door.

Out on Duke of Gloucester Street many fine coaches were rolling toward the Palace, and brown coachmen, footmen and postillions vied with the gentry in gorgeousness of attire. Gentlemen on horseback accompanied their ladies in fine chariots. Coats of arms emblazoned on the carriage doors proclaimed the noble

The Governor's Ball

occupants, to those in Virginia who understood English heraldry. The scene was further brightened by British naval uniforms from a man of war which had lately arrived and was anchored on the York River.

Sally was too young to accompany the Wythes and her parents and older brother and sister, but with Libby and Enos for bodyguard, she fared forth to see and envy, and to anticipate her own participation, in the future, in similar gay scenes. Poor little Sally, little did she dream of the drab and frightening days ahead!

At the intersection of Duke of Gloucester Street and the palace she saw Daniel McCarty, a near neighbor at home. He was accompanied by Cupid, one of the McCartys' negroes, about his age and his boon companion. Daniel and his father were staying at the Raleigh Tavern. Danny had been her favorite playmate ever since she had known how to walk. He had teased her mercilessly, protected her and adored her always. She knew that the McCartys were in Williamsburg and she had hoped she would see him in the swelling throng that now surged toward the Palace. Liberty, gay in red bandana and clashing colors, kept tight hold of her hand. With Liberty on one side and Daniel on the other, and with Enos and Cupid bringing up the rear, Sally and her little party made their way, looking with interest at the occupants of the coaches. There was Mrs. Fairfax with her handsome husband, George William Fairfax, and his father, William Fairfax, President of The King's Council. Mrs. Fairfax had been Sally Cary of Williamsburg. As the Fairfax coach passed, Sally saw the proud and animated face of this lady whom she considered beautiful but felt quite sure her mother did not like, for Mrs. Mason was quiet and conservative, and Mrs. Fairfax was lively and gay.

The Fairfaxes and Masons were old friends, however, and older perhaps than any of them could say, for grandmother Mason's people, the Thomsons, had come from Yorkshire as had the Fairfaxes.

Before reaching the Palace, our little party left the crowd and turned into a side footpath. In this way, they approached the kitchen rather than the main entrance of the Palace. Sally, however, caught a glimpse of the chariots and horsemen approaching the gate where the ladies were assisted in alighting by flunkies in livery and gold braid. There the guests passed under the iron grill and entered the Palace. Sally noticed that the gateposts were surmounted by the lion and unicorn of Great Britian. It was all very impressive and thrilling.

At the brick dependency which housed the Palace kitchen, Liberty's friend, the Palace cook, greeted them. Liberty had made this arrangement in advance, for the cook here had been at the Fanshaws' years ago and had also had the good fortune to leave that unhappy house. Here in Lord Botetourt's household she was now a person of importance. Dinner was over and Louisa could leave the clearing up of her pleasant kitchen to her minions.

Under her guidance the party took a devious route around the garden, finally taking their position at a point where they were hidden by box hedges. Here they could see through the open rear door of the Palace, through the beautiful drawing room and into the ballroom itself. There Sally saw Lord Botetourt receiving his guests. She saw her sister treading a minuet with a young British officer, and suddenly, there on the gravel path of the governor's garden, she was seized by her own escort Daniel McCarty, and with him stepped to the same minuet her sister danced within the Palace. Daniel was grown into a handsome boy, full of mischief and with a winning way.

"Miss Sarah Mason will marry Daniel McCarty," he said, "before any of those young dandies succeeds in marrying her sister."

At that, Liberty intervened. "An' Miss Sally Mason is going home now and fast," she said, "befo' the Mistress say, 'Liberty, has you lost yo' mind, keepin' that chile up so late?' "

Retracing their steps to the kitchen. Louisa whispered to Liberty, "Dat devil-man—Mista Fanshaw's in Williamsburg. You get home an' don't you go outa Mr. Wythe's house without

Enos, you hear?" Liberty's brown face went gray. "Oh, Lawd, Louisa, has he seen you?" "He knows where I is," Louisa replied. "Lawd Botetourt paid him a lot of money for me. But you is somethin' different. He mad you is at Mista Mason's. He shore hates Mista Mason for marrin' Miss Ann! That's why, even after all dese years he wants to git you back. He knows Miss Ann and Mista Mason sets great store by you!"

The walk back to Mr. Wythe's was more of a flight than a walk. Daniel and Cupid saw them home, but once arrived, Sally was whisked into the house without time for a courteous "good-night."

Poor Liberty was in a state of abject terror until the family returned from the ball and her beloved Miss Ann reassured her she had nothing to fear. Fanshaw, she said, had left Williamsburg the night before.

After the ladies had retired, George Wythe and George Mason walked for a while in the garden behind the house. Down the righthand path they walked, the architecturally laid out garden on their left and the succession of plantation buildings on their right. They heard the horses' occasional stamping and noisy sighs in their stalls, saw a stable boy closing the coach house, and Mason noticed the compact and efficient arrangement of the line of neat, well kept, white clapboard buildings. The fragrance of moist earth and box was sweet in the evening air as they turned into the grape arbor at the foot of the garden, traversed its length and returned on the well laid brick walk, toward the dimly lighted house.

Mr. Wythe told his friend of the meeting of the Burgesses three days before and gave him details of the formation of Virginia's Non-importation Association for which the resolutions had been written on Washington's request by George Mason himself. He then described how the Burgesses had drunk the royal healths, and health to the much liked Governor Botetourt.

"He is a good fellow," Wythe said, speaking of the Royal Governor. "If they would send us more like him, we should make better progress over here. May God in his infinite mercy spare him to us for many years!"

They had also drunk, he said, to a lasting union between Great Britian and her colonies and to Constitutional British Liberty in America. His voice underlined the word "constitutional."

A year later the affable and popular Governor Botetourt would be dead and replaced by the choleric and undiplomatic Lord Dunmore, who would find himself challenged by conditions with which he was temperamentally unable to cope.

Mr. Wythe's walk in the garden with his guest was interrupted by young men's voices in the hall, and through the open door, he and Mr. Mason saw George Mason Junior and two other young men, both red-haired. The first was square shouldered and with an alert quick step. The other was tall and moved with the long easy stride of a woodsman.

The butler was directing them into the garden and, with the lights in the hall behind them, it was at first difficult to see their faces. As they drew nearer, Mr. Mason recognized Thomas Jefferson of Monticello, and young George Rogers Clark from the valley of the Rappahannock. The Clarks were kinsmen of the Lewises at Kenmore. Mr. Mason had not seen this young man in several years and was impressed with his increased maturity. Clark must, he thought, be about two years older than his son George, about eighteen perhaps. Thomas Jefferson seemed to know him intimately and explained that his friend had just returned from the Ohio where he had been surveying on the frontier to which he must shortly return. He had examined Fort Necessity where Colonel Washington had fought under General Braddock. He had gone down the Monongahela to Fort Pitt and made, so Jefferson said, some drawings of the ruins of Fort Duquesne, which the French had blown up rather than allow it to fall into the hands of the English. Mr. Jefferson's enthusiasm was contagious and George Rogers Clark's personality was compelling. George Mason had been keenly interested in the Ohio and the western frontier for many years. The hour was late but, before Thomas Jefferson and George Rogers Clark withdrew, Mr. Mason had elicited a promise from young Clark to return with him and his family to Gunston Hall.

9

THE MORNING AFTER THE BALL at the Governor's Palace, Mr. and Mrs. Mason said their goodbyes to the charming Wythe family and set off with their retinue for Gunston Hall. Young George Rogers Clark had appeared promptly, and accompanied them. The men were all on horseback, Mrs. Mason, Nancy, Sally and Liberty rode in the coach. Enos was on the box beside the coachman. The long coach trip was more amusing to the young people than to Mr. and Mrs. Mason, who were eager to be home. The first night was spent at Ruffin's Tavern,[58] an inn near the ferry across the Pamunkey. Its history was linked with William Claiborne and the early days in Virginia. Supper was served on the trestle table in the earth-floored kitchen below ground level. Great logs filled the eight-and-a-half-feet-wide fire-place. The foundation walls were of huge stones brought from England in the early days, when the Capital was at Jamestown, and the massive rafters across the ceiling looked as if they had been part of a ship. Shutters at the small, high, horizontal windows had been placed there to protect the people within from Indian arrows. It was necessary to go out of doors to reach the rooms upstairs, there being no connection in the house between the basement and the first floor. Mr. and Mrs. Mason had a room whose windows looked out upon the swift-flowing, tidal Pamunkey River, the wide marsh upon the opposite shore and Ruffin's Ferry which they had just used. Across the river and marsh, lights glimmered faintly on the plantation of Eltham, the home of Mrs. Washington's younger sister, Mrs. Burwell Bassett. Nancy and Sally had a room, connected with their parents' by a tiny passage which ran through the brick construction of the two massive outside chimneys. Through a small window in this corridor they could see the quarters where Liberty and Enos and the other negroes were housed. Someone was playing a fiddle and a sweet minor chant floated up to the girls as they prepared to retire. The young men's rooms were on the floor above but they, with Mr. Mason, would linger in the taproom below, long after the ladies had gone to sleep.

The taproom, that evening, was full of distinguished guests. Mr. Burwell Bassett and Mr. John West,[59] two gentlemen of the neighborhood, had stopped to hear the latest news from Williamsburg and for a toddy. Mr. Patrick Henry was also staying at Ruffin's Tavern on his way home. The two young Georges, Mason and Clark, spoke little but listened with rapt attention to the great orator's every word.

The succeeding nights of the journey were all spent with friends along their way. The last night, they stayed near Fredericksburg with Mr. Mason's brother-in-law, Mr. Selden of Salvington, the widower of his little sister Mary. They arrived at Gunston Hall the next day, in time for dinner. When they turned into the four-mile drive from the King's Highway to the house, the horses pricked up their ears and quickened their pace and, as they approached the stable on the right, the horses within whinnied a noisy welcome and the handsome stallion, Vulcan, in the meadow, added his royal voice.

At the house, the children and negroes gave them a warm welcome. Ann was relieved to see that the boys' tutor wore a smile and that the boys had a look of well-being. Beck had baby Betsy in her arms and little John clinging to her skirt. Nan Old Gate with the fair haired, nine year old Mary was coming through the arched doorway in the high paling that hid the quarters and the kitchen.

Occoquan Nell and House Nell stood together in this doorway. Diomed, the son of old Orion, raised his beautiful, clarion, hound voice in greeting and made himself heard above all the others. Ann counted them all at a glance, smiling with happiness at being home. The negro boys Dick, Tom, Sampson and Yellow Jim led away the saddle horses and Cato, Mr. Eilbeck's old butler, left to Ann by her father's will, stood holding open the door. It was a happy homecoming and George Rogers Clark, who was also one of a large family, ever from that day on had a sense of belonging at Gunston Hall. This was only the beginning, for him, of many visits, and years later, he wrote to Mr. Mason: "continue to favor me with your valuable lessons; continue your reprimands as though I was your son . . ."[60]

With George Junior he fished and hunted and explored Dogue's Neck, shot sora in the marsh and drank from the nearby spring. The day of his departure came too soon. Fate had marked him for the road to the northwest and these people belonged to the Old Dominion, but the bond between them was, perhaps, a symbol of future national unity.

George Junior returned to his studies, and Nancy, her auburn curls bent over her fine sewing, dreamt of the red-haired frontiersman until some other charming cavalier appeared upon the scene.

Many were the people who found a welcome at Gunston Hall in those happy days. The Cockburns from Springfield were the most intimate and frequent visitors, for their plantation of Springfield lay next the Mason lands. Mrs. Cockburn, who had been Anne Bronaugh, was a cousin of George Mason's. Martin Cockburn was an English gentleman from Jamaica. They had no children of their own and shared Mr. and Mrs. Mason's interest in the young Masons. Anne Cockburn was never too busy with her own efficient housekeeping to give help or advice, or even instruction to the Mason girls who were good potential plantation mistresses.

The year 1770 brought the last little Mason. Small Thomas was born that year and there were now three babies in the nursery, John four, Betsy two and the new wee mite Thomas, for whom the silver christening bowl, with the Mason arms, was brought forth for the last time in that generation.

Sunday at Pohick Church

Life was punctuated by visits from neighbors and by visits to neighboring plantations, by the coming and going of the great winged ships to England, by plantation duties, different for the boys than for the girls, by the breaking in of new colts, training the pups to hunt and retrieve, fishing and hunting and the occasional shooting of a deer in the deer park for venison.

On Sunday there was the drive to Pohick Church, the old church below Gunston, for the new church was not yet built. Here the forefathers of the planters were buried and here the living gathered to affirm their faith. In pleasant weather they lingered to talk while the horses stamped and whinnied at their hitching posts and many a flirtation flourished over the lichen-covered slabs and tombstones. Here young Daniel McCarty, stooping to see the long lashes under Sally Mason's primrose-trimmed bonnet, promised her the pick of his setter Diana's new litter.

Life was so peaceful, established and secure, it seemed no change could ever occur, no event mar the beauty of such a settled order.

10

IT WAS QUITE TRUE that Peregrin Fanshaw had left Williamsburg the day before the Queen's Birthnight Ball. His way lay through Fredericksburg and Dumfries to Colchester, and the ferry near there, which belonged to the Masons. This ferry would transport him across the Potomac River to his plantation on the Maryland side. It was not, however, his intention to return home that evening. At Dumfries he drew rein before the house of Mr. Richard Graham, brother-in-law of Sarah Brent. A negro appeared to take his horse and Fanshaw threw him the reins, but with no smile or affable word of greeting. Word spread quickly from the stable to the kitchen and from the kitchen to all parts of Mr. Graham's house that "dat devil man, Mista Fanshaw" was there.

Sarah Brent was comfortably settled on the window seat in one of the front windows of her sister Jane's drawing room. Her needlework lay neglected on the brocatelle cushion beside her, and she was lost in a novel lent her by Betty Lewis of Kenmore. She found it as engrossing as Mrs. Lewis had promised and was therefore completely surprised by Fanshaw's entry.

There was no light of pleasure in his fathomless black eyes as he regarded her, but rather an acquisitiveness and a sullen look of challenge. Sarah flushed uncomfortably but held out her hand courteously. "I'm sorry Dick and Jane are out," she said. Fanshaw brushed this aside. "I see you read novels. The romantic idea is, after all, not repugnant," he remarked. "I'm on my way home from Williamsburg. Can your brother-in-law put me up for the night? I should like to see him."

He walked rather like a bear, with head and shoulders forward and abnormally long arms hanging loosely. Sarah had once felt the strength of those arms and she shuddered involuntarily as he moved to take a chair. Crossing his legs and leaning back, he continued to regard her sullenly. "Why won't you marry me, Sarah?" he asked abruptly. "I been askin' you for twenty years. Don't you know I'm a rich man? You could have almost anything you wanted at Royce Hall. It needs a mistress—has for years!"

Now that they were fairly embarked upon the old, unpleasant question, Sarah's courage rose and she determined to end the annoyance of these unwelcome proposals. "Peregrin," she said, "I don't love you. I don't even like you. I remember too many unpleasant, unforgettable things—the beautiful dog you killed because he didn't learn fast enough to retrieve the grouse you shot; the glorious horse you murdered riding him to death when you were angry; the poor helpless negro of George Mason's you incited to kill one of your bad overseers and then had the negro shot at Alexandria last year, and his head displayed at the courthouse! Do you think I would put myself in your power for all your ill-got wealth? What protection would your wife have when the devil himself controls your great strength?"

"By heaven, Sarah," Peregrin exclaimed, "you're a pretty woman now! Anger lends you just that charm you once lacked! Sorry, my girl, but I want you more than ever!"

It was true that the years had dealt kindly with Sarah Brent. Her little figure had once been too emaciated, and now, although she was still slight, she was no longer too thin. She had also acquired a spiritual assurance and dignity. Her skin had always been clear and fresh and the band of gray which now ran back from her forehead through wavy, light brown hair, gave her added distinction. Peregrin Fanshaw surveyed her with a satisfaction which Sarah found even more annoying than his anger, which she had expected to provoke.

"It is true," he said, in a surprisingly quiet voice, "that in my youth I sowed my wild oats and did many things of which I am ashamed, but I am ready to settle down and prepare for a respectable old age. And you, Sarah, what do you think your old age will be like? There is nothing for a maiden lady here in the Old Dominion. As it is, you are everybody's housekeeper and everybody's aunt, especially in times of trouble or illness. At Royce Hall, on the other hand, you would be mistress. You would bring order from chaos. No doubt, you would even make me behave! And I should be proud of you," he added lamely, for his tongue was unaccustomed to pleasantries.

For a moment Sarah regarded him with evident uncertainty, but her reply was definite. "No Peregrin, I must first see evidence of that future respectability you describe. Show me that I can respect, even admire you and perhaps I may reconsider. When a man has set his plow in a furrow it is hard to change to another furrow. This you must do first, and without my help."

Peregrin pulled himself up with a gusty sigh. "Well then," he said, "I'll be on my way. No doubt I can put up at the inn at Colchester tonight. I'll not trouble you with my unwelcome presence."

Sarah rose and held out her hand and he kissed it awkwardly, stumbling into Uncle Ben in the hall. The old darky, fearful for Miss Sally, whom everyone loved, had stood hidden in the hall in case of need, for all the negroes knew and feared this unwelcome caller. The old man's frail strength would have been of little help had Fanshaw grown ugly, but Sarah knew why he was there and she was touched.

She saw Fanshaw's horse brought out and watched his departure with relief. His words lingered in her memory, however, "everyone's housekeeper, everyone's aunt." Well, that had been her life for a long time now, and if it were to continue that way to the end of the chapter, she would fill it with as much kindliness and beauty as God gave her grace to use.

11

THE YEAR 1773 was to be unforgettable for the family at Gunston Hall. The fifth American George Mason was then a young man of twenty, Nancy was eighteen, and the youngest of all, little Thomas, was three years old. He was the last baby, in the nursery upstairs, in the room above his parents. John and Betsy had graduated to other rooms. The autumn started happily enough. There was a play and a ball in Annapolis. George and Nancy accompanied their parents, and the weather being fine, they went by boat and under sail most of the way. The play was a delight, but the ball—! Nancy—sweet, unspoiled Nancy— found herself a belle and, being a woman, she was not unaware of her father's and her brothers' pride in her. Also, she met a Mr. Johnson who took all the dances he could capture and left a dream in her heart which would blossom in later years.

In November, Mrs. Mason was ill but no one was greatly worried and she seemed to recover. Winter began with a succession of sleet and ice storms, peculiar to that part of Virginia. As the season advanced, the children, as well as their elders, became aware of the deepening seriousness of the times they were entering. The Masons' neighbors, the Fairfaxes, closed Belvoir and sailed back to England. They were greatly missed and their going seemed to crystallize the division of thought between the Tories and the pro-Colonists. There was a growing sense of foreboding at Gunston Hall, and this was made acute by the fact that Mrs. Mason was now frequently very ill. She rested a great deal, and although she insisted she was not ill, she was far from her old cheerful and vital self.

One evening shortly before Christmas, Mr. Mason rode up to the house from a meeting of the Fairfax County court at Alexandria. On these occasions, Mrs. Mason always met him in the hall with a welcoming smile and questions about the current county problems, about changes in local taxation, the repair of roads and about the cases tried that day in court. Young George had joined his father at the courthouse on that particular day, and as they entered the hall, shaking the wet snow from their riding boots and absently allowing old Cato to take their greatcoats, Mrs. Mason knew from their voices that something was amiss. She hastened down the hall toward them and her husband said at once, "There is serious news from Boston. A group of citizens there, disguised as Indians, have boarded the three British merchantmen I told you about, and have thrown the cargoes of tea into Boston harbor." Ann gasped—"You mean," she said, "the ships Mr. Samuel Adams hoped to persuade to return to England with the tea still aboard?"

George propelled her gently before him into the study and young George followed. "There was a Town Meeting," her husband explained, holding his hands to the cheery blaze as Enos pulled off his boots and put on his slippers which lay on the hearth. "Mr. Adams dismissed it with the ominous words, 'This meeting can do nothing more to save the country.' There was a heavy storm that night, and while it was raging a party of citizens incognito and dressed as Indians, though no one thought they were, boarded the three ships and dumped the cargoes overboard. The next day, as the news spread, it was evident that conservative public opinion in Boston approved this amazing action. It is even believed that some of the most respectable citizens who had been at the Town Meeting were among the so-called Indians. The situation looks very serious."

That evening, at their supper of oyster stew, white corn muffins, tea and syllabub, the Masons discussed foregoing the tea

which was such an agreeable part of their evening meal. They
decided to use what they had but to buy no more. Over the
English silver tea service, Mrs. Mason's face appeared as grave
and anxious as her husband's. What impasse were the colonies
approaching? The candles flickered in a momentary draught as
the wind hurled icy rain against the windows of the pleasant
Chinese Chippendale room. Old Cato, with a nod to one of
his dining room boys, ordered another log on the flames, and a
little shiver ran around the table as if each of those gathered
in the candlelit circle felt a presage of disaster.

Mrs. Eilbeck came and went frequently that winter, between
her Maryland home and Gunston Hall. She was anxious about
her daughter,[61] who was all she had left now that she was a
widow. She felt that Ann was overtired and doing too much
and that Miss Newman, the new governess, should do more to
help her. Miss Newman was a dried up little person, excellent
in the classroom but not very companionable outside. Mrs. Eilbeck wished that she herself were younger and could be more
help. Finally she became really ill and was obliged to stay at
home.

A few weeks after news of the Boston Tea Party reached the
Masons, their own family situation took on an aspect even more
sinister than the public news. Mrs. Mason's room was the scene
of its usual winter activity. A large work table at the foot of
the bed was covered with garments of warm homespun in the
process of being cut out by an old white woman, Mrs. Tugate,
the mother of one of the overseers.[62] The snip, snip of her scissors
was accompanied by the desultory conversation of three younger
women who were busy basting the garments together as soon as
they were cut out. Mrs. Mason and Nancy were examining the
material for flaws in the spinning and weaving, and keeping an
eye on the work of the sewing women. Mrs. Mason looked tired
and flushed, and from time to time she looked out at the storm-
tossed trees which bordered the garden, and at the grey and
angry waters of the Potomac in the distance. Occasionally she
put her hands to her temples, and then with a little shake of

her head went back to her work. At last she said, "Mrs. Tugate, the storm is strengthening. Put up your work. You and the girls must go home."

The work was folded neatly and carried upstairs to a wardrobe where it was kept. Nancy summoned the houseboys, who carried away the work table and extra chairs. The women curtseyed and said their good-nights to the mistress. Little did they dream it was for the last time.

Nancy was concerned, however, at her mother's appearance and still more anxious when her suggestion of a rest before supper was readily accepted. She called Liberty, who always knew what Mrs. Mason would like, and with a horrible fear clutching at her heart, mounted the stairs to her own room.

There had been another meeting of the County Court, but this time when George returned, Ann was not waiting in the hall. Alarmed, he hastened into her room and found Ann in bed looking feverish and ill, and Nancy, Sally and Liberty with her. She was shaking with a chill in spite of her feather bed and the covers the girls were piling on her. She managed to smile through her chattering teeth, and when George reached under the covers for her hand he found it moist and hot.

"Isn't it s-s-silly, George," she said, "all these covers and I am cold!" George Mason's quiet voice reassured everyone, "You are having a chill, my dear. It will pass. Liberty, take the hot water bottle out to Nell. Tell her not to make it too hot and bring it back yourself as fast as you can."

"Oh," Ann murmured, "I feel better already, now that you are here."

For Mrs. Mason to be ill was an unheard-of catastrophe. True, there were nine Mason children whose arrivals had been crises in the life at Gunston Hall, but although everyone else had been ill, and Mr. Mason most frequently of all, Mrs. Mason, until this winter, had always been there to encourage them and assure them all would soon be happy and normal again. Now it was evident that the mistress of the house was very ill. George Junior was sent to fetch Dr. Craik,[63] who came at last, from

across the Potomac. He looked grave, but cheered them a little
with his kindly manner and promised to return in the morning.
George Mason's show of calm was all for his family. A dread
he dared not name was at his elbow. That evening passed and
many mornings, noons and nights. Ann seemed to recover again
and again, only to become still more gravely ill.

From the latter part of the 17th century till the middle of the
19th is known as the "Dark Period" in medical history. Thirteen
years before Ann was taken ill, Benjamin Franklin had founded
the Pennsylvania Hospital in Philadelphia for sick and wounded,
but it was more of an almshouse for the poor than a hospital in
the modern sense.[64] Ann Mason had been stricken with what,
in her day, was called a "slow fever", a term still used in some
parts of the country. The care given Ann Mason in 1770 contributed little to her comfort. She tossed feverishly in a feather
bed. No fresh air was allowed to enter her room. Dr. Craik
ordered milk, with a dash of rum in it, by way of nourishment,
and the children and negroes went freely in and out of her room.
Her voice grew weaker and weaker, but she continued to assure
them that she would soon take a turn for the better, and as she
smiled when she said she did not feel too badly, they almost
believed her.

The Cockburns, from their neighboring plantation at Springfield, rode over every day. Martin Cockburn, an understanding
and gentle Englishman, came to help in any way that he could
even if it were only by listening to the latest development in the
stricken household. Anne Bronaugh Cockburn, his wife, and
George Mason's cousin, helped and advised Nancy, whose
eighteen-year-old wisdom was sadly taxed, to keep the house and
workrooms running smoothly.

To the children, their mother's illness seemed continuous.
Actually there were ups and downs until the dreadful last weeks,
when she sank steadily. At last, on the 9th of March, the end
came just before the dawn, gently and quickly. George held her
hands in his and received her last smile, though this time it was
only a faint flicker.

Our forefathers did very little at times of bereavement to save the sensibilities of a sorrowing family. From sitting up all night with the body, to draping themselves in deepest mourning, everything was done to inflame rather than to relieve their grief. Mourning clothes for the family could not be bought at a moment's notice and had, therefore, to be prepared in advance. Mrs. Cockburn had not been willing to suggest to Nancy, Sally and Mary that they make mourning clothes while they still hoped their mother might live. She had therefore written Sarah Brent and begged her to come to Springfield, and unknown to the Mason family, to help her prepare mourning for them all. Sarah had been an indefatigable worker in this large task and also in keeping up the courage of the Gunston Hall family. When young William Mason rode over to Springfield before daylight on the 9th of March to tell the sad news, Martin and Anne Cockburn wakened Sarah, knowing she would wish to go with them and that the Masons would want her. On their arrival, Dr. Craik was still there and Enos had been sent to fetch the woman who habitually performed in that neighborhood the services for the dead, which today would be the duties of an undertaker. George Mason had gone back into Ann's room and closed the door. No one dared enter. Nancy, Sally, George and Thomson stood stunned and weeping in the hall, and Liberty and Nell gave vent to genuine grief. Colonel Eilbeck's Cato opened the door. His old face, once a smooth bronze, was almost as grey as his hair. He had carried Ann on his shoulders when she was a baby and on this last night he had not deserted his post in the hall. Ann's spirit, like a gallant ship, had set sail with many loving watchers to wave farewell.

As the group from Springfield entered the hall, little Sally Mason flung herself into Anne Cockburn's arms. Sarah Brent went straight upstairs to the younger children, whom she guessed correctly, had not been told and must have the news gently broken to them. A few minutes later, George Mason came quietly out of his wife's room, on his face the look of frozen grief. Sarah Brent came down the stairs at that moment. She had little Thomas in her arms; five-year-old Betsy and seven-year-old John, tearful but quiet, were clinging to her skirts. Mason paused for a moment, as if he wanted to speak. A muscle in his cheek vibrated uncontrollably, and then, without a word, he passed them all, went into his study and closed the door behind him. There, sinking down upon an armchair by the cold hearth, he crossed his arms on his small writing table, dropped his head upon his arms and wept.

Under the ministrations of the Cockburns and Sarah Brent, the mechanism of the house began to function, slowly at first but with growing efficiency. The necessity of tasks to be performed was a godsend to the older children, and their wise friends refrained from doing too much upon that first day. It was Nancy who finally, encouraged by Sarah Brent, went into her father's study with some hot tea, while Enos built up the fire and brought warmth into the cheerless room. Nancy was not her father's favorite, but she most closely resembled her mother, and Sarah Brent was right in selecting her to open that closed door. George Mason held out his arms to her, and Nancy, setting down the tray, flew into them. There were no words spoken between them for none would have been adequate. As soon as he relaxed his arms about her, Nancy brought him the tea, and asked gently what he had been writing. Without a word, George Mason put into her hands the family Bible, and through her tears, Nancy read the only written description of her mother which has been left to posterity. Her father had written:

"In the beauty of her person and the sweetness of her disposition she was equalled by few, and excelled by none of her sex. She was something taller than the middle size and elegantly shaped. Her eyes were black, tender and lively; her features regular and delicate; her complexion remarkably fair and fresh. Lilies and roses (almost without a metaphor) were blended there, and a certain inexpressible air of cheerfulness and health. Innocence and sensibility, diffused over her countenance, formed a face the very reverse of what is generally called masculine. This is not an ideal, but a real picture, drawn from the life, nor was this beautiful form disgraced by an unworthy inhabitant.

'Free from her sex's smallest faults,
And fair as womankind can be,'

she was blessed with a clear and sound judgment, a gentle and benevolent heart, a sincere and an humble mind, with an even, calm and cheerful temper to a very unusual degree; affable to all, but intimate with few. Her modest virtues shunned the public eye; superior to the turbulent passions of pride and envy, a stranger to altercation of any kind, and content with the blessings of a private station, she placed all her happiness here, where only it is to be found, in her own family. Though she despised dress, she was always neat; cheerful, but not gay; serious, but not melancholy; she never met me without a smile! Though an only child, she was a remarkably dutiful one. An easy and agreeable companion, a kind neighbor, a steadfast friend, a humane mistress, a prudent and tender mother, a faithful, affectionate, and most obliging wife; charitable to the poor, and pious to her Maker; her virtue and religion were unmixed with hypocrisy and ostentation. Formed for domestic happiness, without one jarring atom in her frame! Her irreparable loss I do and ever shall deplore, and though time, I hope, will soften my sad impressions and restore to me greater serenity of mind than I have lately enjoyed, I shall ever retain the most tender and melancholy remembrance of one so justly dear."[65]

As the first days and weeks passed, George Mason was at first too overwhelmed by his loss to be aware of anything else. Then his moments of intense grief began to alternate with periods of concentration upon his new responsibilities. He must now be both mother and father to his poor little orphans, as he called them.

Many years later when little John, now seven years old, was an old man, he would still remember the sadness of those days, the hush that hung over Gunston Hall, his mother's burial which he witnessed dressed in black and standing beside the open grave, the other children and the servants always in tears, his father pacing back and forth between the house and the little family burying ground on the edge of the lawn, and how the silence in the lonely house continued even when April and May spread their carpet of spring flowers and scented the air with sweetness.

The negroes' sorrow was tinged with superstition, and the children, who always knew what the negroes said and thought, and the negroes, who always knew what the children said and thought, reacted upon one another. A certain nameless fear of the supernatural, on the part of the younger children, followed the funeral. Some weeks after Mrs. Mason's death, the first thunderstorm of the season rumbled and flashed across the sky in the early evening. When the family were gathered in the parlor after supper, Sally said, "It is going to rain. We must see that the windows are closed." Nancy looked anxious, a usual expression for her now, and said, "The bulls-eye window in the attic is open. I was up there this morning, looking for an extra spinning wheel. It was musty and I opened the window." George fixed fourteen-year-old Thomson with an elder brother's terrifying look and said, "Thomson, go up and close it." Now Thomson and Mary had just come from Nan Old Gates' Quarters. Mary threw him a look of deep sympathy, as a blinding flash of lightning was followed by a clap of thunder directly overhead. She knew that his manhood demanded that he go and go alone. But she also knew he had heard young Sampson, in Aunt Nan's kitchen that afternoon, say he had been followed by a "speret" from near the buryin' ground as far as Hereford's Spanish oak. Thomson rose with nervous alacrity and took a candle in a pewter candlestick from among the collection kept on the hall table near the foot of the stairs. It was the custom for each guest or member of the family to take a lighted candle from this table when mounting the stairs for the night. Large candlesticks were for the men, smaller ones for the women. Thomson, with his large candle, ascended the stair, went into the room where the wardrobes of linen and sewing were kept, and opening the door to the little attic ladder, went slowly up into a world of shadows.

The candle flickered uncertainly and he stumbled into an old spinning wheel, out of date now, but one of those ancient objects which had come from the Old Plantation, where his grandparents had lived on the river bank. He seemed to be entering a world of the spirit. Forgotten treasures and necessities of forgotten people surrounded him. Another flash of vivid lightning filled the round shape of the bulls-eye window with light, and thus given his bearings, Thomson bore down upon the object of his quest. He closed the window, receiving a shower of raindrops on his face, and secured it carefully, but as he did so, his candle flickered and went out. He turned and retraced his steps as another flash revealed a white shape moving relentlessly and noiselessly toward him. Something brushed his right cheek his shoulder and his hand. He eluded the horrid unknown by a sprint and feint which would have done credit to some football playing descendant. He almost fell, rather than ran, down the steps, crossed the upstairs hall and then, with dignity and a measured tread, he descended to the family group in the parlor. Sally and her father were now at the card table. Nancy and Mary were sewing. George and William were standing by the fire talking. George looked up. "Oh, thank you Thomson," he said, and added. "By the way Nan, weeks ago I had the little black sailboat out and the jib tore. I brought it up to the house and had Sampson hang it in the attic to dry. Then, with everything happening, I forgot it. Could you have Mrs. Tugate look at it and see if it can be mended?" Thomson's chin dropped as he stared fixedly at his brother. Only a faint sound escaped him but two people in the room knew at once what had happened. Mary gave him a look of complete understanding which he caught before she dropped her eyes again to her sewing; and his father's quick, aware glance was full of comprehension also, though he too remained silent and Thomson was grateful.

To Nancy, looking back on it all later, it seemed that the negroes had saved her very reason. Not only was their sympathy deep and warm and comforting, but they made her laugh when no one else could have done so. They laughed easily. They laughed at themselves and at each other and she laughed with them. Of course some had as a special gift, what has been called "spiritual elegance."[66] Others were endowed with the gift of laughter. Old Cato, Nan Old Gate and Enos were in the first group, but Liberty, Sampson, one of the kitchen boys, Old Beck, the ancient Mammy, and many others were in the second. Liberty was Nancy's delight as she had been her mother's.

Nancy called her one day to come into the garden and see the countless hummingbirds that had been attracted by the blossoms of guelder rose and Persian jessamine.[67] "No Mam, Miss Nancy, I doesn't want to come out. I's 'fraid a hummin'-bird!" "Oh now, Liberty," Nancy began, but Liberty explained from her post of safety on the octagonal porch, "One of um stuck his bill in me once." Nancy laughed and came back to the house. The sun lighted her glorious hair and her garden basket was filled with flowers. Who was to say if Liberty had not meant to make her laugh?

Old Beck's humor was of a different sort. Mrs. Mason had tried vainly all her life, as Mrs. Eilbeck had done before her, to break the old negress of a most peculiar habit. It was not vulgarity, for there was no vulgarity in the early American negro. If they have acquired it, it has been by evil associations. Old Beck, who had been Ann Eilbeck's old nurse and had later cared for each of her infants in turn, loved to see "the quality" and enjoyed all social occasions. She had her favorites among the ladies who came to Gunston Hall and enjoyed taking their wraps when they arrived, but the services she performed for them were always completed by the administration of a smart spank upon the appropriate part of their anatomy just as they left the room. For years Mrs. Eilbeck, Mrs. Mason and now Nancy or Sally had apologized to the astonished ladies saying that only those Beck admired received the spanks.[68] The ladies usually laughed but Nancy always felt the explanation inadequate, although she laughed too.

Sarah Brent had become accustomed to Old Beck's honors. She always laughed gaily and delighted the old woman who laughed with her. She and Mrs. Cockburn were often at Gunston Hall now. George Mason had been making his will and was convinced that he would soon follow his beloved Ann. The childless Anne Cockburn was an excellent housekeeper, and Sarah Brent had neither husband, nor children, nor home. Had it not been for them, Nancy's young shoulders would have been laden beyond her ability to carry on.

Peregrin Fanshaw was not the only one who had noticed that Sarah Brent had become a distinguished and charming middle-aged woman, and Martin and Anne Cockburn, who had always loved her, determined to have her at Springfield as much as possible. They counted upon her graciousness and tact to draw the heartbroken planter out of his lethargy and back into the stream of human and political life. Little did they expect the villainous Fanshaw to take a hand in it.

12

WHILE THE Mason family were trying to regain their equi-
librium after the death of Ann, Americans were becoming
more and more aware of a strong bond between the colonies.
Mounted messengers travelled back and forth carrying news
between the north and south, and wherever people gathered,
opinions were expressed and discussed. Gunston Hall, on the
main road between Boston and Williamsburg, could not remain
secluded for long. Its master's wisdom and his knowledge of
English and Virginian political history made his advice an imperative need. It seemed at times that the prominent men of the
colonies made many demands upon George Mason's judgment,
as well as upon his hospitality. Nancy often felt overwhelmed
by her responsibilities to the four plantations on Dogue's Neck,
and also by the increased number of unexpected visitors from
Charleston, Richmond, Philadelphia, New York and Boston, not
to mention her new family cares.

One morning after Mr. Richard Henry Lee and Mrs. Lee had
spent the night, and Colonel and Mrs. Washington, with Jack
Custis and his bride, Eleanor Calvert Custis, had come to dine,
Nancy went about her household duties with a sense of fatigue
and a fear of consequent inefficiency. Mrs. Tugate, the cutter
of all the plantation garments, had been kept at home by the illness of someone in her family. Nancy, with the help of one of the
less skilled women, had undertaken to cut some cotton cloth for

necessary garments. There were interruptions; among other things, Betsy had fallen downstairs and frightened them all by a momentary loss of consciousness. Late in the afternoon, poor Nancy discovered a mistake in the cutting. The material appeared ruined. She had the work in her own room, and after the sewing women had gone home, she laid the stuff on her bed and studied it to see what could be done. There her father found her in tears and utterly discouraged. Perhaps her tears were a relief to him, too. He held her tightly in his arms and told her over and over what a comfort and help she was to him. The cotton cloth, he said, would be easily replaced and was unimportant. What was important to him was her happiness. He told her how proud he was of her, and said that she had managed better than he would have believed possible.[69] He recalled to her the conversation at dinner the night before. Colonel Washington and Mr. Lee, he explained, hoped ardently, as he did himself, for reconciliation with Great Britain. It was this deep concern, he said, that had made them both so grave and quiet. Mrs. Washington, as they all knew, was sad in the company of youth, remembering the death of her seventeen-year-old Patsy less than a year before. No doubt she recalled the many occasions when Patsy had accompanied her to Gunston Hall for Mr. Christian's dancing class and for a party or hunt. Jack and Nellie Custis, a recent bride and groom, were much in love and very happy. Nancy, sensitive to the feeling of those around her, had turned the conversation to a happy subject, the boyhood of Mr. Lee and Colonel Washington. They were the same age, and Ferry Farm, George Washington's boyhood home, had not been too far from Stratford of the Lees for the boys' frequent trips back and forth. Now, at the dinner table at Gunston Hall, Nancy had soon had them laughing over boyhood recollections. "The other day," Colonel Washington said, "I was going through some old papers and came across an old letter of yours, Dick. You said you were sending me a pretty picture book. I had to write a letter thanking you, I remember."

"I remember those books," Mr. Lee replied thoughtfully, "and I remember the poem in your letter which you said someone else had written. I remember your pony Hero, too, and how Uncle Ben used to lead him when you rode over to see me.[70] What good days those were, George!"

Mrs. Lee had been one of George Washington's first loves, as well as her husband's. George Mason had thought of them both as small boys in the years when they were all growing up, for he was seven years their senior. Now, however, they all had many memories of the golden past and Nancy had skilfully kept the conversation gay and easy. In this Mrs. Washington had helped her. One had lost her mother, and one her daughter, during recent months and there was a tender understanding between them. Now George Mason made his daughter feel his appreciation also, of her gift of hospitality. He would be grateful for this gift many times in the years to follow.

By the spring of 1774, the political outlook had grown even darker. The British announced their intention of closing the port of Boston, which would paralyze the city. This punitive measure was to become effective the first day of June.

The Virginia House of Burgesses passed resolutions of sympathy, proclaiming a day of "fasting, mourning, and prayer" for that day. George Mason was in Williamsburg at the time on private business. We can see him at the Raleigh Tavern, writing a letter to Martin Cockburn, his faithful friend, and guardian in his absence, of the family at Gunston Hall. His letter is dated May 26, 1774 and in the formal manner of his day it begins "Dear Sir:" and is signed "your affectionate and obedient servant." Mason had arrived, he wrote, on Sunday and had found everyone "so engrossed in the Boston affair" that he had been able to do nothing so far about his Charter rights. Obviously he had become himself "engrossed" for he writes: "Matters of that sort here are conducted and prepared with a great deal of privacy, and by very few members; of whom Patrick Henry is the principal. At the request of the gentlemen concerned, I have spent an evening with them upon the subject, where I had an opportunity of conversing with Mr. Henry, and knowing his sentiments, as well as hearing him speak in the House (of Burgesses) since, on different occasions. He is by far the most powerful speaker I ever heard. Every word he says not only engages but commands the attention; and your passions are no longer your own when he addresses them. He is in my opinion the first man upon this continent. . . ."

Further on he wrote: "Enclosed you have the Boston Trade Act and a resolve of our House of Burgesses . . . they would wish to see the example followed through the country. Mr. Massey (the minister at Fairfax) will receive a copy of the resolve from Colonel Washington; and should a day of prayer and fasting be appointed in our county, please to tell my dear little family that I charge them to pay strict attention to it, and that I desire my three eldest sons and my two eldest daughters, may attend church in mourning, if they have it, as I believe they have."

He added that he was tired of the town and asked to be tenderly remembered to his children.

Folding his letter, Mason absently affixed the seal. His thoughts were at Gunston Hall, where, upon the following Sunday, George, William, Thomson, Nancy and Sally would leave for church dressed in black, as at the time of their mother's death. He sighed, and with the letter in his hand, went into the corridor and started downstairs. As he did so he suddenly became aware of many voices and footsteps, and the door of the Raleigh Tavern opened to admit Patrick Henry's tall spare form. He entered, talking gravely with Peyton Randolph, whose handsome, saturnine face expressed the most intense concern. Colonel Washington followed, close at Randolph's elbow. As he crossed the threshold, he leaned forward from his great height to catch Mr. Henry's words. These three commanding figures were followed by all the other burgesses from the house. Mason, pausing on the lowest step of the stair, understood that it was indeed serious business that had brought these men to the Raleigh. Patrick Henry, catching his eye, invited him with a commanding gesture to join them.

The Burgesses Meet in Raleigh Tavern

The innkeeper and servants were busy clearing the Apollo Room, and as Mason fell into step beside his neighbor and friend, George Washington, he learned that the irate Governor had prorogued the burgesses and that they were here to continue their business unmolested. This had happened five years before when Lord Botetourt had dissolved them for protesting that Americans should not be transported to England for trial. Now, once more, the low hum of indignant voices filled the Apollo Room at the tavern as some eighty-nine Burgesses[71] found seats, and negroes moved in and out bringing more chairs. As soon as quiet was restored, Richard Henry Lee, his bronze face flushed but his voice deep and steady, read a set of resolutions he had prepared. It was agreed that the Boston Act enslaved them and it was again recommended that no purchases be made from England. George Mason, who was four years older than Randolph, regarded his face with interest. He, like Thomson Mason, had studied law at the Inner Temple in London, for he was the son of the King's attorney for Virginia. Mason remembered him well when, as a promising young man of twenty-seven, Peyton Randolph had himself been appointed King's attorney. Then sixteen years later had come the Stamp Act, and this conservative Englishman had opposed Patrick Henry's "Stamp Act Resolutions", but a year later, he had resigned as King's attorney and been chosen moderator of the privately convened Assembly. There he had been largely responsible for the non-importation agreement of 1769 and he was now Chairman of Virginia's Inter-colonial Committee of Correspondence. Randolph's face was flushed now, as he listened to Mr. Lee's resolutions and the color rose and fell across his cheekbones. His long, slim fingers beat a silent syncopation on his chair arm. "He is typical," Mason thought, "of the men I have grown up with, conservative, loyal gentlemen, headed, against their will, into what turbulent, unknown sea!"

Now the way was being prepared for the calling of a Continental Congress.

Patrick Henry's dark, piercing glance questioned Mason, who

nodded agreement, and Washington leaned toward Randolph and whispered to him. The first step would be a provincial convention. Would he preside? Randolph also nodded assent.

The following August, Randolph did indeed preside over the provincial convention and later he was president of the first Continental Congress, September 5th till October 22, 1774. He was re-elected the following March and died of apoplexy in Philadelphia in October 1775.

That Sunday in Williamsburg the burgesses "with Speaker and Mace," proceeded in a body to Bruton Parish Church to hear "a suitable sermon on the Boston Port Act." Lord Dunmore, with his lady in the governor's great square pew, must have brought a troubled and confused heart to his prayers. A pitifully small human spirit, he had been given an appointment in one of those vast, unprotected spaces which appear in the history of man, where the winds of destiny sweep from the past into the future and carry all before them. A stouter man than Dunmore could hardly have harmonized the thinking of Hanovarian England with the ideas of the new world about to be born.

George Mason, from a pew in the rear of the church, watched it all with understanding. In spite of his faith in his country and in the parent country, his heart was heavy with foreboding for the young Masons, who at that moment were dressed in mourning and attending Pohick church at home. Englishmen would think through eventually in "a spirit of power and of love and of a sound mind," but what must they endure before those problems were resolved?

At the Raleigh Tavern the following day, Mason encountered Daniel McCarty, who, like himself, happened to be in Williamsburg on business. The senior McCarty's florid face lighted with pleasure at finding his neighbor in the busy and now agitated town. The two men went together into the garden, where, over a glass of madeira, they could discuss the momentous affairs afoot.

"By the way," McCarty said, "I was in Norfolk last week. I

have a boat there under repair. I heard a lot of whispering about the family of shipbuilders, I think you know them—the Goodriches. They're bad actors, it seems, and slippery as eels. No one can accuse them openly of making trouble, but everyone suspects them of crimes from piracy to an effort to widen the breach between His Majesty's Government and the Colonies. Their activities should be watched. Are you riding home with Colonel Washington?" Mason said that was his intention. "Very well then," McCarty said seriously, "I hope you will quote me to him."

He rose, for he had an appointment, he said, at the college.

"I shall be home next week," he added. "Ride over when you can, all of you. We are always glad to see you and I'll see you at Bogges' Racecourse, I hope, too."

Mason assented and they parted cheerily. Mason forgot the Goodriches until they were brought painfully to his attention soon after that conversation.

13

As GEORGE MASON and George Washington turned their horses toward home from Williamsburg, their minds were busy with the coming Virginia convention, now set for the following August. There were about two months in which to consolidate the feeling of Fairfax County as a whole. Mason felt strongly, as did his neighbor, Colonel Washington, that the quick minds in the community must await the slower mental processes of more deliberate thinkers. When the County acted upon so grave a matter as separation from England, it must act with unanimity. At the convention in Williamsburg the ideas of the Virginia counties would be crystallized. The line of action they took would greatly influence the Continental Congress at Philadelphia in September.

Washington understood that George Mason's studied decision to take a conspicuous part in political affairs resulted from his strong sense of responsibility and an incredible knowledge both of English Common Law and of the political history of Virginia, and Washington deeply respected his wisdom.[71a] Before they parted, Mason knew that he had enlisted the man who should play the leading part in the martial theatre of revolution.

As Mason left the King's Highway on the long ride between his own hawthorne hedgerows to Gunston Hall, he knew that he was returning home only to leave again. He knew he must plan to ride to Mount Vernon and to Alexandria often in the immediate future. The knowledge dulled his happiness in the noisy and ecstatic welcome he received. The sight of his sons, George and William, hair rumpled and fishing rods on shoulders, sent a pang through his heart, for they were youths, and he knew they must soon answer a call to arms. When Betsy flung herself into his arms and smothered him with kisses, and Nancy, Sally and Mary lifted their laughing, rosy faces, he could only think how much he wanted to stay, how loath he would be to go.

Supper over and the fire lighted, to dispel the chill of the

George Mason and George Washington Turn Homeward

early June evening, Mason continued to question his family about every detail of their lives since his departure. Yes, they had gone to church dressed in black as he had directed, and Betsy, on a stool at her father's feet, the gold mist of her hair diffused over his velvet-clad knee, added saucily, "And Daniel McCarty said Sally was even more beautiful in black than in her new blue bonnet." She mimicked Daniel's changing voice so exactly that everyone laughed, except Sally who blushed furiously and dropped her yellow head over her sewing.

Young George fixed Betsy with his clear eyes, so like his father's. Well he knew the power of his glance! It was an asset inherited from the Fowkes but it did not wither Betsy, who was made of the same stuff. Seeing she was about to reply, he said quickly, "Father, could you arrange to have me go to this Continental Congress in Philadelphia next autumn? I should greatly like to see it and to hear the speeches." His father promised that he would endeavor to arrange it, and then, thinking of his own coming absence from home, he turned to Nancy. "My dear child," he said, "I have pledged Colonel Washington to a course that will keep us both from home much more than we should wish."

Nancy, her needle suspended, looked at him with her air of sweet seriousness and nodded understandingly.

"I have been wondering," her father continued, "do you think Mistress Sarah Brent would come and make you a long visit? I cannot ask the Cockburns to come and stay. They are kind about coming over constantly but they have their own responsibilities at Springfield." Nancy looked hesitant. "I wonder," she said thoughtfully. "Mistress Brent spends much of her time these days at Dumfries with the Grahams. You know Mrs. Graham's little boy who came here and played with our little Tom? He is a sickly boy and Miss Sally thinks no one can care for him properly but herself. They say she has practically taken him for her own."

"I suppose," Sally put in, "he is the baby she never had. Such

a shame! She is a dear and she has been a slave to her whole
family always, starting with that complaining Bermudian mother
of hers and her cross father, not to mention her sister Mrs.
Douglas, before the Douglases left for Scotland to marry their
children off to Scottish noblemen."[72]

She stopped, out of breath, and suddenly aware of young
George's eagle look turned upon her and full of disapproval.
"Sally," he said, "I hope you won't grow into a gossip. Miss
Sally would hardly appreciate your picture of her family!"

"But they are unkind—" Sally began.

Mr. Mason broke in, "Well this little boy, George Graham,[73]
why not ask her to bring him with her? Should you all like
to have them?"

Betsy squealed and clapped her hands, and little Tom said,
"Oh yes, do, please!"

Their father quieted them with, "Hush, honey, and how do the
rest of you feel?"

The vote proved unanimous and it never occurred to any of
them that Sarah Brent might refuse to come.

Sarah Brent received Nancy's letter and one from George
Mason at her sister's house in Dumfries. The Grahams had
gone to Richlands, the old Brent plantation above Aquia Creek,
and Sarah had been left at home with only the four-year-old
George for company. She sat in his nursery now. It was raining,
a gentle June rain which had laid the dust on the road, just beyond the lilacs and the white picket gate in front of the house.
A great puddle lay in a low area in the brick walk under the
mulberry tree. Little George was standing on the window seat,
his small nose flattened against the pane, and Sarah, beside him
in the window embrasure, regarded the raindrops which danced
like silver-winged fairies on the surface of the great puddle. Her
inner mind was with the Masons at Gunston Hall, but with her
eyes, she observed every motion of the raindrop fairies. She was
remembering the day Ann Mason died, lovely, gentle, gracious
Ann. Sarah had met her first in Virginia as George Mason's
bride. There had been a party at the Mercers, at Marlborough.

George Mercer had invited her, Sarah remembered. What a failure he had made of his life, bringing the stamps from England for the hated Stamp Act! He was completely innocent of all knowledge of how the Colonists would react. Among the most irate of the Colonists was his own father, George Mason's guardian and instructor. Young Mercer had gone back to England, his career as a diplomat ruined. Sarah had thought him charming that evening at Marlborough, and Ann Mason had made much of her, helped her do her hair more becomingly, and introduced several young gallants Sarah had not met before. George Mercer had drifted out of her life, but Ann had remained and the acquaintance had ripened into real friendship. Sarah remembered again the night Ann had died, the pitiful children huddled together in the hall and George Mason with his head on his arms in his study. She knew well enough that Anne Cockburn had tried to marry her off to George Mason but he had given no sign of wanting her and Sarah had respected his grief for the peerless Ann. Now his letter lay on her knee. "Would she come and stay with his poor little orphans? Little Tom would be very happy if her nephew would come with her." Yes, she would go, and if Jane gave her permission, George Graham should go also. It would be good for the pale child to run and play in the gardens and fields at Gunston Hall.

A week later, Sarah was settled with all her small belongings in her old room at the Masons, and George Graham in the old nursery with Thomas, both four-year-olds under the care of Liberty. They were kept out of doors as much as possible, for George Mason was ill with one of his painful attacks of gout.

Sarah's warm, kindly presence appeared to be a good tonic. He was relieved to have her there and said so frankly. Sarah flushed with pleasure and asked about the papers he was working on. They seemed to cover every table, chair and bureau in his room. Mason outlined generally for her his idea of the Fairfax Resolves. Sarah was a good listener and in a short time she had not only grasped his idea but put the papers into order, so that whatever he wanted at the moment was ready to his hand.

By the time George Mason had sufficiently recovered from his indisposition to ride to Mount Vernon and confer with its master, Sarah Brent knew almost by heart that document known to us as the Fairfax Resolves. It has come down to us as written by the Clerk, Robert Harrison, Gentleman, in the Court House in the town of Alexandria, on Monday, the 18th of July, 1774.[74] It called for the "preservation of our common rights and continuing the connexion and dependence of the said Colonists upon Great Britain, under a just, lenient, permanent and constitutional form of government."

In Virginia the leaders of public thought sought, during those summer days of 1774, to draw from the different counties a unanimous expression of what should be done by the proposed Continental Congress. At the same time, they strove to arouse public feeling to give aid to Boston. Colonel Washington opened a subscription for assistance to that unfortunate city. Money, flour and wheat were donated, and these served two useful purposes: the needy of Boston were assisted; and the other colonies, in coming to their aid, were welded into a unity unknown until then along the Eastern Seaboard.

When George Mason turned his horse in at the Mount Vernon gateway, he was at once aware that Fairfax County, from the hills on its western boundary to the Chesapeake, was giving generously to that distant Massachusetts town. Horses and mules, laden with sacks of wheat or flour, and men in buckskins, toiled along the drive where formerly, gentlemen on blooded horses had been a more familiar sight. This strange cavalcade turned off on the road to the landing where Mason saw a schooner[75] at anchor. The sound of distant voices indicated the loading of the supplies, not for England now, but for some secret destination as near Boston as possible.

At the house, Colonel Washington and his lady greeted their neighbor with unfeigned pleasure. Under the stress and pressure of recent events Washington's manner had become even graver and his speech more measured than before. Martha Washington's greeting was even warmer and more cordial than was natural to her in quieter days. Her tiny figure seemed to emanate hospitality and welcome. George Mason, whose per-

sonality has been described as commanding more respect than
affection, did not for a moment chill the warm friendliness of
her nature. Perhaps her kindliness was especially appreciated by
this warmhearted but reserved Virginian.

After one of the delicious dinners for which Mount Vernon
had become famous, the two gentlemen withdrew to Colonel
Washington's office. Mr. Mason spread out his papers, and
sentence by sentence, they went over the Fairfax Resolves together.

"In them George Mason uttered the first clear and emphatic
statement of the rights of the American Colonies. There were
twenty-four of those Resolves. They are justly famous, for in
them, Mason first gave expression to the basic political philosophy of which he was to become champion. In these Fairfax
Resolves, Mason first asserted the right of independence. In
them he laid down many of the basics of our national government: that taxation and representation are inseparable; that the
importation of slaves must stop; that the colonies had a free and
natural right to make their own laws."[76]

What a quiet but important moment it was when Washington
and his neighbor sat in a sunny room at Mount Vernon and discussed together this now famous document, Mason reading,
Washington interrupting from time to time. The low murmur
of their voices could not be heard beyond the open windows and
yet their words still echo down the centuries.

When Mason rose to go, it was arranged that, at the County
meeting, to be held in Alexandria on the 18th of July, he would
himself present the Resolves he had written.

Colonel Washington's body servant, Billy, appeared, as if by
magic, with some excellent madeira, and Mason suddenly remembered some cuttings for Mount Vernon, left forgotten in his
saddlebags. Both men, sipping the madeira, reverted happily to
the more congenial and familiar role of planter. Political anxieties were put aside, for the moment at least, and botanical discussions took their place until the friends parted and Mason rode
away.

14

In the meantime, at Gunston Hall, life had flowed along in its accustomed measured rhythm. Nancy and Sally had sailed across the Potomac with young George and William, for two or three nights with the Fowkes at Gunston Hall in Maryland. Rinaldo Johnson would be there to beau Nancy, and Sarah had urged them to go on her account especially. The younger boys were hunting "tarrapkin" on the Gunston Cove side of Dogue's Neck.

After dinner, Mistress Brent suggested that Betsy and she take the pair of four-year-old boys and go down the road through the pasture to Hallowing Point for apples. An ancient apple tree grew near the old quarters. It had been planted long ago in the days of the Old Plantation. It was gnarled and windblown from its exposed position on the point of land which extended far out into the river, but every year it bore a luxuriant burden of small, rosy, lady apples which were made into delicious jelly by House Nell.

Sarah's suggestion met with noisy approbation, and, sending for Enos to follow them and shake the tree, the little party set off through the kitchen garden. Liberty was happily at work there among the herbs, which, next to the children, were her most cherished task. Sarah had put on a gown of brown homespun and comfortable shoes. They laughed and chattered as they crossed the pasture and George Graham and Tom tried to lure

the calves but without success. Sarah noticed that some negroes
were at work on the rails of the fence, repairing the damage done
by a recently fallen tree. Betsy kept up her usual stream of soft,
chirruping conversation, half with Sarah, half with Enos who
was her especial favorite.

Arrived at Hallowing Point, everyone fell to work gathering
the ruddy nuggets of apples. Enos hoisted his powerful frame
into the tree and laughed melodiously as he shook the branches
and the children scrambled for the falling fruit. Even Betsy was
too busy to talk.

Suddenly, noiselessly, from around the point and its fringe
of tall rushes, a canoe bearing two men shot inshore, close to the
little party of fruit gatherers. The men in the canoe appeared as
startled as Sarah and the children. She recognized them both at
once. Peregrin Fanshaw was paddling the canoe, and the heavy,
black-haired man opposite him was one of the Goodrich brothers,
boat builders in Norfolk. Sarah had seen this man often in
Dumfries where he had had business from her merchant
brothers-in-law. She was too startled to speak and the men held
a whispered conversation, too low for her to hear. She noticed
that Goodrich held a board with a piece of parchment nailed on
it. He appeared to be drawing a chart of the shore line. Obviously their business was nefarious and they had believed the
Dogue's Neck shore line to be deserted. Perhaps Fanshaw had
heard that the Masons had gone to the Fowkes' and had thought
Gunston Hall momentarily vacant.

Sarah, standing under the old apple tree, the three frightened
children clinging to her homespun skirts, watched him as a
fascinated bird watches the snake which is about to strike.
Fanshaw had evidently decided on his line of action. He shot
the canoe straight toward her, beaching it partly on the turf. He
leaped out with the anchor in his hands. Speaking to the children he said: "Run up to the house and call someone to help
Miss Sarah." As they scampered away he held up the anchor.
"This," he said, "will anchor you to the bottom of Chesapeake
Bay. No one will mourn your loss. You might have been a

convenience to George Mason, whose heart is buried with his wife, but you will be where you can do me no harm since you refused to do me any good."

As he spoke he took her with one hand by the throat. Holding the anchor in the other hand, he prepared to slip its rope around her neck. At that moment, Enos, like a wildcat, dropped squarely upon his head and shoulders from the limb of the tree directly above. Fanshaw, taken by surprise, staggered backward and fell under Enos' weight; Enos, holding him down and pulling him toward the river at the same time, succeeded in throwing him into about two feet of water among the rushes on the river's edge. It was Enos now who pressed strong brown hands to Fanshaw's throat. Meantime, Goodrich heaved his heavy but muscular body from the canoe and started to Fanshaw's aid. It all happened in the proverbial twinkling of an eye but Sarah, still clutching a staff, with which she had pushed aside the leaves in her search for apples, sprang at the new enemy and struck him smartly on the back of the head with her impromptu cane. He fell, but not without his hunting knife, aimed expertly before he lost consciousness, at Enos' neck. A red tide colored the wavelets around the three men. Calls and halloos from the pasture road told Sarah that the negroes in the pasture were coming. Fanshaw recovered himself from beneath Enos' limp body, threw the unconscious Goodrich into the canoe and pushed off so swiftly that, by the time help arrived, he was out of sight around a bend in the shore. But as he rounded the point, Sarah saw him draw his revolver and aim directly at her. Nothing happened. The waters of the Potomac had soaked his gunpowder and saved her life. She saw to her dismay, that the boys, John and William, attracted by the shouting, were running toward her, and by the time the three negroes arrived, followed at a distance by the weeping and frightened children, Sarah had pulled Enos from the water and was endeavoring to stop the flow of blood from his jugular vein. They all knew it was hopeless, and as the little party, carrying Enos' limp form, came between the negro quarters and the kitchen, toward the house,

George Mason appeared in the arched doorway of the wall between house and kitchen.

Sarah could never recall exactly what happened next. She knew that Liberty uttered a low, strangled cry, that House Nell took charge, that the three negroes carried Enos to his quarters in what they called Logtown, beyond the stables, west of the house. The colored preacher appeared, as if by magic, and then she had a distinct picture of George Mason, on his knees beside Enos' cot, of his gentle hands examining the wound, and of his white drawn face and his tears pouring unhindered down his cheeks. Finally, convinced that there was no hope, Mason gathered Enos' brown hands into his own and leaning over, with his face close to the beloved brown one, she heard him cry,

"Enos, Enos, hear me! You must hear me, Enos. I wanted you to be free. It was you who did not want it! Now I swear before God that if it is in my power to move the colonies, your race shall be free of servitude and my people shall be free of the sin of owning slaves."

Then suddenly dropping his head on the dead negro's chest, Mason sobbed as if his heart were broken. After that everything was a blank to Sarah Brent. They told her she had fainted, and that Mason had carried her into the house and laid her on the bench in the hall while he questioned the three men who had come to her rescue.

Later that evening, when Miss Newman had taken the children off to bed, a pale and sad Sarah told George just what had occurred. It was hard to live it all over again but she forced herself to recount every detail she could remember. When she finished George Mason had her cold hand in his, encouraging her to complete her horrible, halting tale.

"Enos would have given his life for me," he said. "As it was, he gave it for you. Enos always knew my thoughts, even when we were boys. He knew I needed you, Sarah."

He paused, rose and taking Sarah's hand, led her to a divan where he could be seated beside her.

"I should be a poor sort of bridegroom," he continued. "I've nothing of the old fire left, for I think my heart died with Ann. There is only tenderness and kindness left—and a few more years perhaps. But such as I am, would you have me?"

Sarah looked stunned and, misunderstanding her silence, he continued diffidently. "I was wondering all this today as I rode home, but I meant to ask you under happier circumstances." Sarah's eyes were filling with tears. "I can't marry you—not now, George," she cried and began wringing her hands. "I had a letter today from my sister-in-law at Woodstock. My father is ill and she has always felt put upon that he lived there. After all, it is his home, but she resents the responsibility of his care. She says, either I must come there to live again, or Jane must take the old gentleman to Dumfries to make his home with her. He would be unhappy, for he loves Woodstock where he has lived all his life. He is an old man and he needs me."

"I need you too," Mason put in gently and Sarah, turning to him, gave him both her hands. "Not to mention," she said, "how much I need you. But it can't be—not yet. When my father has gone, if you still want me it would make me happier than I dare to think."

"Then that is the way it will be, Sarah, and till that time, you are my affianced bride."

"You mean," Sarah asked incredulously, "that you will wait until I am free to marry you?"

Mason laughed and his laughter relaxed them both. "Of course, you silly little baggage. Do you think I am going courting in the neighborhood after all this time, to find a wife? No, my dear, it will be you, or no one!"

"Now I am here," she said hesitantly, "I could stay longer. I could stay till after you read the Resolves at the court house. I should like to know how it goes there. But once I have returned to Woodstock I shall have to stay."

Neither Washington nor Mason could remain a peaceful county squire in the year 1774. In July, at Fairfax County Courthouse in Alexandria, George Mason read his Fairfax Resolves. They were enthusiastically accepted, not only by those crowded in the courthouse on that hot day, but by the throng of people in the square.

In the order outlined by the Colonial Government, the next step was that each of the Virginia counties should send delegates to Williamsburg, there to present their County's Resolutions. In 1774 all these Resolutions had to do with the proper and desirable relation of the colonies to Great Britain. Fairfax County's representatives were George Washington and, since Mason refused to serve, Charles Broadwater in his place. The Virginia Convention now referred to itself as "the late House of Burgesses."[77] Peyton Randolph was still the Speaker, and it was he who laid before that distinguished gathering the Resolutions of the various Virginia counties. More than half the counties had produced Resolutions, of which copies still exist.[78] Among them were the Albemarle Resolutions. Thomas Jefferson, riding to present them, became ill on the way and forwarded them to Patrick Henry for presentation. Feeling ran high, and in addition to the Resolutions brought in, Williamsburg was the scene of heated discussions and the Williamsburg newspaper was publishing a series of articles by Thomson Mason who signed himself "a British American."

The late House of Burgesses, after due consideration of the ideas presented by the different colonies, voted George Mason's Fairfax Resolves the most clearly stated, moderate and representative of public opinion. "The pen of the Revolution," as Jefferson would later term Mason, had written its first words.

The first Continental Congress was to meet in Philadelphia the following September. There the Fairfax Resolves were to prove the sinew and substance of procedure for that and subsequent congresses.

Sarah returned to Woodstock with Washington's congratulations to Mason ringing happily in her heart. She was more proud and happy than she had ever dreamed of being. She and George Mason had agreed that what lay between them should remain a secret, and it never occurred to her that the road back to Gunston would be, for her, a long and hard one.

15

On the 30th of August, 1774, George Mason again rode to Mount Vernon. There he spent a night in company with Colonel Washington,[79] Colonel Pendleton, Mr. Patrick Henry and Mr. Thomas Triplett. These gentlemen were on their way to the first Continental Congress, which was to meet on September 5th, in Philadelphia. Only in influence would George Mason be present when the Fairfax Resolves were submitted to Congress as Virginia's outline for government. He would return home to his duties as father and plantation owner, and as the quiet country gentleman he preferred to be. There were other matters, however, besides the Resolves, which he wished to discuss with Washington. He and his neighbor had been appointed to a committee of twenty-five for Fairfax County to act "in case of emergency." In a few weeks he would preside at a session to create the Fairfax Independent Company of Volunteers. He would, later, refer proudly to this company as "the first company of militia on this continent."[80]

The following morning, Colonel Washington and his guests, excepting Mr. Mason, set out for Philadelphia. Mason turned his horse toward home. His mind was busy now with plans for the Independent Company of Volunteers. It should not exceed one hundred men. The uniform should be blue, turned up with buff, plain yellow metal buttons, buff waistcoat and breeches and white stockings. The men should be furnished

with a good flintlock and bayonet, sling cartouch box and toma-
hawk. "We should agree to keep by us," he thought, "a stock
of six pounds of gunpowder, twenty pounds of lead and fifty
gunflints, at least. We must be masters of military exercise
and be always ready in case of necessity to defend the prerogatives of our sovereign King George III and the just rights and
privileges of our country, our posterity and ourselves, upon the
principles of the British Constitution."[81] "A strong militia," he
thought, "should do away with any necessity of our being taxed
to support British troops to protect us and also from a standing
army quartered upon the colony.[82] That is what they are saying
in Maryland and I agree."

He would draw up a plan[83] for this company of militia and
his mind went over and over what he would say:

"All men are by nature born equally free and independent . . ."

"To protect the weaker from the injuries of the stronger . . ."

"Was that not the reason for government? . . ."

"North America is the only great nursery of free men now
left upon the face of the earth."

"All power is derived from the people . . . we should wear
it as a breastplate . . ."

But now he was home, remembering at once his loneliness
and his eagerness to see his children. Peyton Randolph might
wonder why he shrank from public life. Well, he need not
explain his reasons to the world!

The great brass lion's head knocker on his own door gave
him a look of leonine understanding.

That autumn of 1774 there was bloodshed on the western
frontier, bloodshed which, in Virginia, was later considered the
start of the Revolution.[84] Truly, it seemed that Lord Dunmore's
evil genius had placed him in the position of royal governor to
Virginia at that time. Sinister news came to Williamsburg. The
family of an Indian chief had been murdered by white border
settlers, and the Indians were massing to punish the white
intruders and to halt their advance into what is now West Virginia, Kentucky, Ohio and Indiana. The families on the frontier
called on Lord Dunmore for aid.

George Mason, discussing the evil tidings with his neighbor and friend Martin Cockburn as they stood together at Bogges' Racecourse, was greatly relieved to learn that Dunmore himself had set out for the pass through the forbidding Allegheny Mountains and for the valley of the Ohio beyond. Mr. Cockburn reported that Dunmore had called up two divisions from the upper and lower Shenandoah Valley and the second of these divisions had been placed under General Andrew Lewis, one of the gallant Lewis family of Fredericksburg.

It will be remembered that the Ohio country had caught the imagination of George Mason in his youth. In 1749 he had been one of the first members of the Ohio Company, that group of farsighted men who had for their object the colonization of Virginia's western territory and the promotion of trade with the Indians on the Ohio. They had obtained a grant of 600,000 acres of land, mostly west of the mountains and south of the Ohio,[85] and they had sent out Christopher Gist, that able frontiersman who had led where many followed. All this was when George was a young man, but through the busy years which followed, his interest had never faltered. It had been kept alive first by his feeling for "the land". To Virginians of Mason's day, Ohio was the new land, the symbol of the future, the child of the Old Dominion and the home of Virginians, still unborn. Secondly, Mason's interest in Ohio was held by his continuous correspondence with that red-haired young frontiersman, George Rogers Clark, now in his fourth year in Ohio. This young adventurer, with his courage, his quick brain and indomitable spirit, wrote often to the older man whose paternal advice he had the wisdom to appreciate. Thinking of these things, Mason turned into the carriage drive to Springfield for a glass of peach brandy with his friend before returning home. As they approached the long, low, one-story house of the Cockburns, Martin Cockburn rallied him gently on his preoccupation. Martin's charming English voice had taken on a touch of the soft Virginia speech.

"My dear George, you will forgive me for thinking your anxiety about the frontier is now as out of place as was my anxiety about earthquakes in Virginia because I came from Jamaica where they are frequent occurrences. How understanding was my bride when she accepted this house I built for her home!"

Mason laughed wryly and looked up at the low rambling house, and as Anne Bronaugh Cockburn greeted them, both men were still smiling. Mrs. Cockburn, a perfect housekeeper and hostess, soon had them settled by the fire, glasses of peach brandy at their elbows, and filled with the sense of well-being she always managed to inspire. However, her questions about news from the Ohio brought them all back to George Rogers Clark, and with feminine, apparent loss of direction, Mrs. Cockburn said: "I didn't want him for Nancy, George."

It was with her words in his mind that George Mason turned his horse toward home.

In the meantime Nancy and young George Mason were winding their way from the landing, where they had just waved good-bye to a gay party of visitors, departing by boat for other Potomac River plantations.

Coming slowly up the path through the pasture, the brother and sister walked arm in arm, and Nancy spoke thoughtfully of a young man who was perhaps at that moment engaged in Indian fighting.

"Mrs. Cockburn tells me," she said, "that the red-headed Clarks inherit their coloring from beautiful, red-haired Mary Byrd of Westover. It seems she was George's grandmother. Mrs. Cockburn says a strain of benevolence comes down in that family, and that the ones with red hair earn the world and then give it away. The dark-haired Clarks, she says, are the money makers.[68] I think," Nancy added, "she was afraid I would lose my heart at sixteen and follow George Rogers Clark to the Ohio."

Her brother gave Nancy's arm a little squeeze and said teasingly: "You are no frontierswoman, Nancy. You had better say 'yes' to Rinaldo Johnson and settle in Maryland instead. My faith, if you don't do it soon, the poor fellow will go mad."

They were in the garden now and William, in riding clothes, his gray eyes wide with excitement, came running down the porch steps and across the grass to meet them. "I met Father at Bogges," he said. "His Excellency Lord Dunmore has returned, but without honor. The Borderers are saying he allowed General Andrew Lewis to fight vast numbers of Indians while he, Dunmore, stayed snugly in camp, hoping for the destruction of the troublesome Americans."

"What of George Rogers Clark?" Nancy asked, as the three walked toward the house. "He is a major under Lord Dunmore."

"He's safe," William replied. "You may depend upon it, for as Father says, he carries a charmed life. Someone said he had gone down the Ohio with some missionaries and intends to stake a land claim beyond the farthest. I'd like to go after him but Colonel Washington says there will be fighting here at home for George and me and that we may be needed soon."

In September George Mason had presided over a meeting of his "committee in case of emergency," and his plan had been adopted for the creation of the Fairfax Independent Company of Volunteers. His son George was among these young gentlemen volunteers. They were under the command of no less a person than Colonel Washington himself, and the uniform Colonel Mason had selected became the uniform of the Colonial Army, now for the first time acquiring the name of the Continental Army. The use of this word indicated the sense of unity that was growing in America. North and South were beginning to conceive the idea of one people, not one people on the Atlantic coast alone, but a people whose western boundary lay beyond vast mountains and unexplored territories.

Col. Mason decreed that William could not enlist at once but must finish his studies. Later, his father would speak with pride of "his coolness and intrepidity" under fire in the defense of Williamsburg. It was George, therefore, the fifth of the name in America, who was first of the Mason family to wear the new uniform of a fledgling country.

In the meantime, more news was coming through from the Ohio. General Andrew Lewis himself appeared in Williamsburg; and in Charleston, Richmond, Williamsburg, Philadelphia,

New York and Boston it became known that a gallant division of Americans had laid down their lives on the frontier in the battle of Point Pleasant, and that their comrades would have murdered Dunmore, the British Colonial Governor, in cold blood for failing to support them, had not their equally angry General forbidden it.

As the news spread through the colonies, indignation mounted. There was talk of "liberty," by which Americans still meant constitutional rights under the monarchy and not independence from the Crown. When the Independent Company of Volunteers was formed in Fairfax County under George Mason's supervision and placed under Colonel Washington's command, everyone referred to the Indians as the menace, for they still were unable to name their dread of England, and this sinister story of Dunmore's perfidy on the frontier had remained only a rumor, until General Lewis himself appeared in Williamsburg and men in Virginia heard the story from his own lips. Lord Dunmore wrote home angrily of the new American Congress. Under the non-importation acts, colonists were ashamed to purchase goods from England, no matter how much they desired them, and Britain's overseas exports were reduced over a quarter of their total of the year before. It was a time of taut nerves and angry disagreements. Men of British descent remembered that they were English, Scottish or Welsh and were hurt and baffled by the parent country's lack of understanding. At this time, January, 1775, Mason wrote:[87]

"Firmly determined, at the hazard of our lives, to transmit to our children and posterity those sacred rights; and thoroughly convinced that a well regulated militia, composed of the gentlemen, free holders, and other free men, is the natural strength and only safe and stable security of a free government, and that such militia will relieve our Mother country from any expense in our protection and defense, will obviate the pretense of a necessity for taxing us on that account, and render it unnecessary to keep any standing army (ever dangerous to liberty) in this Colony, we the Subscribers . . . have freely and voluntarily agreed . . . to enroll and embody ourselves into a militia for this country."[88]

In March, Patrick Henry, at the 2nd Virginia Convention, made a motion for colony-wide militia saying: "As for me, give me liberty or give me death."

Now the tempo increased, pulsating and throbbing in men's veins like a fever. At last, on the 18th of April 1775, a horse's hoofs took up the syncopation, faster and faster, as Paul Revere spread the alarm "through every Middlesex village and farm . . ."

For the British troops had been ordered to destroy the colonies' ammunition stored at Concord. Embattled farmers at Lexington, Massachusetts endeavored to stop them, and at Concord, when the stores were destroyed, the British were finally defeated at the bridge and were thereafter forced to return to Boston.

Before news of this fight could reach Williamsburg, Lord Dunmore had ordered the store of gunpowder there to be secretly removed to Bermuda.[89] On the 20th of April, two days after the battles of Lexington and Concord, the loss of the powder was discussed. Randolph, Nicholas and Nelson succeeded in calming both the governor and the angry people and in preventing bloodshed.

News of the battles at Lexington and Concord reached Virginia on the 27th of April, and Patrick Henry set out at once from Hanover County Courthouse, with a hundred and fifty men, for Williamsburg. As they marched across the country, their number swelled to a great multitude and Henry approached the colonial capital at the head of a formidable army.

Dunmore, his angular figure stiff and resolute, his unpowdered dark hair brushed crisply back from his bony and set face, stood at the green baize-covered table in his library in the Governor's Palace. The sound of drums and marching feet denoted that the men of Williamsburg were hastening to join their comrades. How had he mishandled this unpredictable people and brought himself to such a pass? Nothing in his hard life had prepared him to meet such problems as the colonies evoked. He had ample courage, but courage was not enough. These men were

Englishmen—Englishmen? Yes, but with a difference. They were colonists. "Colonists!" He spoke the name aloud as a term of opprobrium.

At that moment a white and trembling footman announced: "Mr. Peyton Randolph, calling on His Excellency."

Immediately Peyton Randolph's portly figure and impressive succession of chins appeared in the doorway.

"I must show him I am unafraid," thought Lord Dunmore. Aloud he said, jutting out his chin, "Good evening sir. To what am I indebted for this second call?"

Randolph, with the natural majesty of his personality, replied, "Your Excellency hears the approach of indignant Virginians. Englishmen will not submit to coercion, even by Englishmen, and Virginians are Englishmen. You, sir, have caused the powder to be removed from the Williamsburg powder magazine. It must be paid for, as I have already called to your Excellency's attention, and at once. Blood has been spilled in Massachusetts for this cause, and Mr. Patrick Henry approaches the Palace with, I do not know how many thousands of men. There is no time to lose. Tell me where you will meet him, and I will send word. He is encamped at Doncastle's Ordinary."

Dunmore, his eyes flashing fire, his hand toying nervously with the handle of his sword, replied: "You may tell this Mr. er-a-Henry I will meet him at his place of encampment. Neither he nor his rabble are to set foot in Williamsburg, and tell him that, by heaven, if harm is done to me or to the men under my command I will proclaim freedom to the slaves and they shall be armed!"

Randolph bowed and retired with unruffled dignity, while Dunmore barked out commands to subordinates waiting in the hall.

In Doncastle's Ordinary on Williamsburg Neck, north of the town, Lord Dunmore met Patrick Henry's keen, dark look with arrogance and ended by paying twice the value of the powder taken. Henry wrote Robert Carter Nicholas, on the 4th of May:

"The affair of the powder is now settled so as to produce satisfaction to me, and I earnestly wish to the Colony in general."[90]

But it was as if they had all been caught up in the wild swing of an Indian dance. Around the Governor's Palace events swirled faster and faster. George Mason[91] expressed the general feeling of the colonies when, in writing to a friend in England, he said:

"The Americans were pretty unanimous before, but the acts of the present session of Parliament, and the blood lately shed at Boston have fixed every wavering mind, and there are no difficulties or hardships which they are not determined to encounter with firmness and perseverence."

The Second Continental Congress met in Philadelphia that May, and Colonel Washington appeared in uniform. Young George Mason, also in uniform of buff and blue, had his wish of attending a Continental Congress, and his father, always concerned for his children's well-being, wrote his old friend Richard Henry Lee[92] on May 31, 1775:

"My son George has a mind to spend some days in Philadelphia while the Congress is sitting, and as he has been very little in the world, and young fellows are too apt to fall into bad company in a place where they have few acquaintance, I must presume so far on your friendship as to recommend him to your notice and advice, for which I am sure he will be thankful."

With emotion and pride young Mason saw his Colonel, that tall, quiet, clear-eyed man whom he had known all his life, appointed General and Commander-in-Chief of all the Continental Forces. What dreams of glory, never to be fulfilled, must have thrilled the boy's heart. A few weeks later, when the Congress had issued a "Declaration of the Causes of Necessity of Taking up Arms" and Washington had proceeded to Boston to begin military operations, George Mason V had been attacked by the same dread disease, a gout or rheumatism, which had followed his father from his youth.

Heartbroken as he was to return, ill, from the very door to glory, there was one man in Virginia more miserable than he.

This was John Murray, Earl of Dunmore, lying in his great red-brocade-curtained bed in the palace at Williamsburg. He listened, as a spring storm rolled over the Virginia capes. The peals of thunder and flashes of vivid lightning seemed but an expression of the threat that hung over His Majesty's government in Virginia. There had been no troubles so puzzling as these during his governorship of New York. To be sure, there had been troubles there recently also. The "Children"—no, the "Sons of Liberty"—that was the secret New York organization that had encouraged resistance to Britain's Navigation Acts. What a troublesome lot these colonists were! Well, when he was relieved from this office, he hoped he could go back to the House of Lords. Ah, his years there had been the best he had known!

A brilliant flash of lightning followed by a terrible clap of thunder revealed a white figure in the doorway. Dunmore was on his feet in an instant, the pistol from his bedside table clutched in his hand, but Lady Dunmore's sweet, tremulous voice ended his alarm: "John, John, my dear. What a fearful storm!"

Throwing herself into his arms, she burst into tears.

"Oh John, when can we leave this savage country? I am afraid—not for myself but for you and the girls. What is to prevent these revolutionists from stealing the powder left in the magazine out there, and murdering us all?"

Dunmore drew his trembling lady over to a chair by the fireplace, stirred the faint red embers and placed a log upon them.

"Listen, my dear," he said gently. "You have nothing to fear. Any unauthorized person who enters the powder magazine will be killed instantly. I have caused a trap to be placed upon the door. Once it is opened by anyone ignorant of this arrangement, the guilty party will meet instant death. Here," he added, "put your poor little feet to the blaze. They are like pieces of ice."

"How did all these difficulties start, John?" Lady Dunmore asked, quieter and less frightened now.

"I often ask myself the same question," her husband replied. "These colonists seem to think that as Englishmen they are entitled to the same privileges they would receive at home. They forget that Great Britain finances her colonies only to support herself. And now my dear, back to bed. No one knows what tomorrow may bring forth."

A few days later, when the June roses were opening in the Palace Garden and the warm Virginia sunlight brought out the fragrance of the box, some young bloods, sipping their ale at the Raleigh, concocted a plan which as it turned out, ended His Majesty's rule of the Colony of Virginia. After dark, it was agreed they would go to the powder magazine and see for themselves just how much gunpowder remained in Williamsburg.

Before the next morning dawned, two of them lay at death's door and the flash which had wounded them had set off the charge of resentment which, throughout the south, had been ready to explode. By the 8th of June, Lord Dunmore had moved the seat of government to the *Fowey*, one of the battleships on the York River, and he and his wife and daughters were living in the ship. Never again did a British Royal Governor live in the Palace at Williamsburg.

16

WITH THE DEPARTURE OF LORD DUNMORE, Virginia was left without a governor. The House of Burgesses met, but for a year their meetings were ineffectual for there was seldom a quorum. Then came the Battle of Bunker Hill, a stiffening of colonial resistance throughout the colonies, and the appointment of Colonel Washington as Commander-in-Chief of the Continental Army. His appointment left his seat vacant in the Virginia Convention, which was now meeting in Richmond. George Mason was urged to take Washington's place. This he refused to do, but consented to serve in the third convention, which met in July, 1775.

In the meantime, life in the Mason household had proceeded with the usual series of small crises which arise constantly in a large and lively family. All winter the smaller boys and girls had studied under tutor and governess. There had been the usual sequence of duck shooting, fox hunting, and deer stalking; and for the older girls, spinning, sewing and knitting and all interspersed with parties.

That Spring of 1775 brought its wealth of roses as usual. In the garden at Gunston Hall the bushes of guelder roses[93] lifted their clusters of creamy blossoms over the hedges of box. In the marshes, the peepers raised their spring chorus and the mockingbirds sang, as they had sung for centuries, their spring love songs.

But it was a season of farewells and anxiety for the family

at the Hall. In their hearts each knew that the world was sadly awry.

Young Daniel McCarty came to say good-bye to the Masons and especially to Sally. He looked very handsome in his new uniform, and when he rode away he carried near his heart his lady's little lace handkerchief, still moist from her tears. Rinaldo Johnson came, too, to say good-bye to Nancy. He sailed across from Maryland where Colonel Smallwood was training those gallant men who would hold the line on Brooklyn Heights in the coming bloody battle of Long Island. Rinaldo was going upon some secret mission. He could not say what it was nor where he was being sent. But on this June evening, his thoughts were not of gallantry but of the beautiful girl whose heart he had finally won. They stood in the many-sided porch on the garden front of Gunston Hall. The moon, hanging low over the Potomac, enhanced, if possible, the beauty of Nancy's winsome face, and the two great rose bushes on either side of the steps filled the air with the fragrance of their blossoms.

"How can I bear to leave you?" he said—the old, old words as full of meaning as if they had never before been spoken. "We must think of your coming back," Nancy replied. "That is what I shall think of every night and every morning when I say my prayers."

Young Johnson stooped and kissed her, suddenly, roughly, and turning fled from her, through the garden, down the terraced hillside to his boat, waiting at the landing.

George Junior, crushed by his illness and disappointment, was his father's gravest concern. Not only was Mr. Mason in fear for his son's life, but he was overwhelmed to see him start upon a career of suffering which he had himself endured. Dr. Craik tried in vain to encourage both father and son. At last he suggested that, as soon as the boy was strong enough to do so, he ride to the Springs and try the healing of their waters. Consequently, the month of June saw his departure.

News of the violent little battle of Bunker Hill, on June 17th, shook the colonies and was followed by a strange period of waiting, a sinister calm before the storm. George Mason worked early and late preparing his plantation for his own future absences on political work, and mid-July found him in Richmond at the third Virginia Convention. From there he wrote Martin Cockburn, speaking of the importance of the business before them. This, he said was ". . . to raise forces for immediate service . . . to new-model the whole militia . . . to render about one-fifth of it fit for the field at the shortest warning . . . to melt down all the volunteer and independent companies into this great establishment . . . to provide arms, ammunition, etc. . . . and to point out ways and means of raising money; these are difficulties indeed!"[94]

The carefully organized Independent Companies in Virginia were now to give way to Minute Regiments[95] and, as Mason wrote Cockburn, this was just one of the many tasks he was engaged upon. Another, close to his heart, was that the colony should export no flour, wheat or other grain or provisions of any kind, beginning the 5th of August, and Mason presented a resolve to this effect, and, in his letter, he said that he enclosed a copy of a resolution he had presented on non-exportation providing that, after August 5th, no flour, grain or other provisions be shipped from the colony, and he added, ". . . I have been a good deal pressed by some of my friends to serve at the Congress but shall firmly persist in a refusal, and thereby hope to prevent their making any such proposal at the Convention."

But a month later he wrote Martin Cockburn again, saying:[96]

"I have found my apprehensions in being sent to this Convention but too well verified."

In spite of all he could do he had been called upon publicly in the Convention to give his reasons for refusing to go to the next Congress. It was for him an overwhelmingly embarrassing experience to find himself upon his feet, among many strangers, explaining that his motherless children required his presence at home and that his own ill health made it impossible for him to serve. It only added to his discomfort when he read sympathy in the eyes of the President of the Convention.

"I felt myself," he said, "more distressed than ever I was in my life."

"But," he added, "my getting clear of this appointment has availed me little, as I have been since, in spite of everything I could do to the contrary, put upon the Committee of Safety; which is even more inconvenient and disagreeable to me than going to the Congress. I endeavored to excuse myself, and begged the Convention would permit me to resign; but was answered by an universal 'NO'."

Through the heat of that Richmond summer, Mason served on a committee which met at seven in the morning and continued till the Convention met. The Convention continued till five in the afternoon, paused for dinner and met again as soon as possible, continuing till ten at night. No wonder Mason was very ill when he returned home! Added to the fatigue of the work, he wrote Washington that, "Mere vexation and disgust (at what he called 'babblers') threw me into such an ill state of health, that before the Convention rose, I was sometimes near fainting in the House."

However, he felt that at the end some progress had been made and that, if the Convention had sat a few days longer, "the public safety would have been as well provided for as our present circumstances permit."

A rumor he had heard in Richmond added to his anxiety. Dunmore's ship, the *Fowey*, was lying off Norfolk and his mind turned back to his conversation with Mr. McCarty who had expressed fear of the Goodriches of Norfolk. No doubt the chart of the Potomac at Dogue's Neck, which one of the Goodriches had made with Fanshaw's aid, was now in Lord Dunmore's possession.

On his return, he stopped at Woodstock to reassure himself that Sarah was safe, and to enquire what precautions the Brents were taking to protect their houses, Sarah's home, Woodstock, and Richlands, home of her cousin, William Brent. Both plantations lay near Aquia Creek, a stream deep enough for ocean-going ships to navigate. It was late in the afternoon when Mason drew rein before the house and surprised Sarah herself in the wide, cool hall. She had placed her father's armchair where any passing breeze would reach him and was reading to him from Smollett's *Tristram Shandy*. Little George Graham, with his aunt as usual, was building a house of blocks at their feet. Sarah put down her book, a look of happiness lighting her face into actual beauty. As servants appeared to take Mason's hat and to help his servant unpack his things, he was aware of Sarah's close scrutiny. He could not hide from her that he was weary to the point of exhaustion. It was a relief to see how quietly and efficiently she took charge of the situation. In no time he was settled in a comfortable room, served by well-trained servants and forced to take the rest he so sorely needed.

Later, in the garden, by a table under a great tree, and looking out over Aquia Creek and the marsh to the Potomac in the distance, Mason and Sarah, with her father and her brother Robert and Robert's wife, talked in low voices of their unbelievably strange situation. It was incredible that British men-of-war and an irate Governor could be a threat to English Colonists. Sipping their madeira, of which old Mr. Brent had farsightedly laid by a large quantity, they discussed the Goodriches—"Gutridges",[97] George Mason called them disgustedly. There were a father and three sons. They had been indulging in out-and-out piracy, playing the British against the Americans and growing as rich as Croesus on their ill-gotten spoils. A look from Sarah warned George Mason that the old gentleman knew nothing of her adventure, and the conversation turned upon the Brents of Richlands, distant cousins of Sarah's but close to Robert Brent, for he and William Brent had both married into the Carroll family of Maryland.[98] William, it seemed, had laid in no ammunition and refused to be alarmed. Old Mr. Brent becoming excited at the conversation, they all dropped the subject quickly by common consent, and Mason realized that the old man had grown frail and was as excitable as a child. The next day before he left, however, George Mason made sure that Robert Brent was doing all he could for his family's safety and that Sarah would be packed inland at the first hint of danger. If his farewell were not sentimental, it satisfied Sarah that he had taken thought for her well-being, and she watched thoughtfully as he rode away.

Back at Gunston Hall, Mason found that his strength was spent. He allowed Nancy to send him to bed and was thankful to lie there quietly, listening to familiar sounds, sleeping, and waking only to sleep again. The drone of the bees at his window, the song of the cardinal, the lilt of Betsy's laughter and of John's and Thomas' little-boy voices were a constant and happy reminder that he had come home. At evening, the mockingbird poured out its liquid, poignant dream of Paradise, seeming almost to recall Ann's presence to his side, while, in the woods beyond the paddock, he heard from time to time the sharp, stuccato bark of the foxes.[99] And there were the evenings when the negroes sang their minor "Hymn Tunes," strangely comforting and satisfying.

Under the spell of his beloved Gunston he was well again at last. His son George returned from the Spring, recovered, for the time at least, and father and son planned together for the tobacco harvest and discussed the ripening grain. Young George joined a company of Minute Men and was made captain,[100] which pleased his father as much as himself.

Summer wore into early autumn and the harvest noon, which cast black shadows on a garden etched in silver, and made Sally and Nancy wistful, lighted British men-of-war; sails set, spray breaking on their prows, on a voyage up the Potomac and into Aquia Creek.

17

At Woodstock, the quiet of that autumn evening was broken by the sound of galloping hoofs on the drive. The Brent family were sitting by the fire after supper, the women sewing, Robert Brent polishing his flintlock and old Mr. Brent near the fire, a plaid wool shawl thrown over his spare knees. Scarcely had they become aware of the approaching rider when a loud knock on the door was followed by the rider's unceremonious entry.

"The Committee of Safety of Stafford Country, sir," he said breathlessly, "give warning that British ships are sailing up the Potomac and are setting fire to tobacco warehouses and dwellings."

The young man saluted and started for the door, which had remained open admitting a cold draught, so that they all shivered with the chill as well as with fear engendered by the unwelcome news. Robert Brent, who had sprung to his feet on the messenger's arrival, hastened to see him to the door and to insure his warning the Brents at Richlands. He ordered the coach brought around immediately while Mrs. Brent ran to wake the children and see that they were well wrapped for a long, cold drive back to friends in the hills. Sarah, reassuring her father and replying as best she could to his quavering questions, prepared him and herself for the dreaded journey. Mrs. Brent refused to leave her husband, and the party in the great coach were soon rolling and swinging along the rutty road to the back country. Sarah, holding the smallest child, endeavored to see that her father and the children were warm, and to calm Little Codger, her own maid, and the two or three frightened negroes they had brought with them. The bright moonlight, which made their way clear, was actually a menace to shore plantations, she thought, for it made it easy for raiding ships to find their quarries. She wondered if George had managed to have ammunition for the Virginia ships stored at Quantico and if there were enough American ships to give them any protection. How carefully he had gone over Robert's plan for her safety in case of this emergency and how tired he had looked! She thought with a pang of his weary, drawn face and the gray hair at his temples. She wondered if she would ever marry him after all.

"Perhaps," she thought, "I could move my father to Gunston and take care of them both."

Ashamed of her impatience with her frail old father, she leaned over, as if to make it up to him, and tucked the robe more snugly around his knees.

Leaning back again, in the rolling and lurching coach, she caught her breath in horror. There, in the direction of Richlands, the sky was red with an ugly glow. Toward Woodstock the sky was serene and dark, but she knew, without a doubt, that Richlands was ablaze.[102]

They arrived at their destination after midnight. Everyone there was asleep, and by the time the family were wakened and the travelers settled in rooms hastily prepared, Sarah was too weary to indulge in futile anxiety. She was wakened toward morning by a severe storm of wind and rain which was sweeping inland from the coast. As windows rattled and the wind moaned and screamed, she wondered if the ships had continued up the Potomac and whether the howling fury without were friend or foe. Was it fanning flames at Gunston Hall, Springfield, and Mount Vernon, or was it driving out the intruder?

Two days later, they were back at Woodstock. All the family were safe, but Richlands had indeed been burned and the destruction of tobacco warehouses further down the Chesapeake

had been ruinous to some of their friends. People said that
Gen. Andrew Lewis, who had led the men of the Shenandoah
Valley at the terrible battle of Point Pleasant, had found at last
his opportunity to fire at Lord Dunmore. His cannon balls had
hit the governor's ship, the *Fowey,* causing no loss of life but
shattering the ship's china, to His Excellency's unspeakable
rage.[103]

George Mason, she learned, had moved his family inland and
had recommended to Mrs. Washington, who was then at Mount
Vernon, that she should leave the neighborhood also.[104] Gunston
Hall and its neighboring plantation houses were safe.

Mason wrote to Washington: "Dunmore has come and gone,
and left us untouched except by some alarm. I sent my family
many miles back in the country, and advised Mrs. Washington to
do likewise as a prudential movement. At first she said 'No, I
will not desert my post'; but she finally did so with reluctance,
rode only a few miles, and, plucky little woman that she is,
stayed only one night."[105]

The storm had been a friend to the colonists, for because of
its intensity, Dunmore had been forced to retire, cursing, no
doubt, the heathenish country where such violent storms came
up without warning.

The following January his ships[106] fired on Norfolk. That
year he sailed back to England, and although he returned later,
he was never again governor of the Old Dominion.

Sarah Brent was not immediately aware of the damage done
to her life by this episode. But her father's stroke, which followed shortly, was no doubt due to that wild night drive with
its attendant fear and hardship and the horror of Richlands'
destruction. Now there was no hope of her marriage while he
lived. Faint as the hope had been, Sarah needed all her courage
and endurance to meet the new disappointment, for her wedding
was now indefinitely postponed.

It seemed that life itself was at a standstill. Sarah's life was
only a small part of the whole. The colonists were impatient
with General Washington because he continued to lay in sup-

plies and for nearly nine months made no move to dislodge
the British from Boston. As later events proved, it was time well
spent, but a country upon the brink of war found it hard to
be patient.

George Mason worked steadily on the Committee of Safety
and wrote Washington his report on their work. He wrote that
they were encouraging the making of saltpetre, sulphur and gunpowder, and establishing a "manufactory of arms." In addition
to the regular work, the committee, he said, was directing the
stations of the troops and calling the minute-battalions and drafts
from the militia, if necessary, etc.[107] As usual, he signed himself:

> "with great respect, dear Sir,
>   Your affectionate and obedient servant
>   George Mason."

As the year wore on toward Christmas, Nancy and Sally, too,
found themselves marking time in a period of endless waiting.
To add to the depression of the family at Gunston Hall. Mr.
Mason suffered another attack of gout in November and was
forced to give up all thought of attendance at the Virginia Convention,[108] scheduled to open in Richmond on the first of December. The two older sisters, taking the younger Mary and
Betsy into partnership, determined that Christmas should be as
gay and happy as their combined efforts could make it, in spite
of the anxieties around them. Going through the pasture to the
woods for holly and mistletoe to deck the house, they came upon
an old negro, Uncle Joe, busily splitting logs for the fireplaces.
Little Jack, the son of House Nell, was squatting on the ground
at his feet and warming himself at the blazing fire, designed to
keep Uncle Joe warm when he rested. This he spent most of
his time doing, so that the number of logs he split only exceeded
by a small number the logs he burned. Nancy called to him
gaily, "Uncle Joe, don't you work too hard now! We can't have
you laid up with the misery for Christmas!"

"No, ma'am, no, Miss Nancy," the old darky replied, his
smile wrinkling his lined old face even more. "I's goin' take

these in fo' Massa's little settin' room in jus' fo' or five minutes now."

"Let Jack help you," Nancy said, "and then send him out to us to help carry in the holly we are going to cut."

She turned laughing eyes to Mary.

"If it weren't for Sampson we should never have any wood in the fireplaces," she said, "and since James has become father's new body servant, he is too high and mighty to give Sampson any help at all with the firewood. I must have the wood box filled in the south guest room," she added to herself, and then, "Sally, shall we ask Mistress Sarah Brent for Christmas? What do you all think?"

And so Sarah Brent came to Gunston Hall for Christmas. George Mason was pleased that the girls had asked her and Sally remarked slyly to Nancy that "Father's gout seems better now that he has something pleasant to anticipate."

Sarah arrived on horseback several days before Christmas and came into a hall hung with holly and mistletoe and obviously prepared for a dance. The younger children were having a party that evening, Nancy explained, and the McCartys were bringing a negro fiddler who was the best in the neighborhood. If Nancy and Sally could not have their beaux, at least there were smaller boys and girls to dance the minuet and *Sir Roger de Coverley* and to play *Pawns for Redemption, Grind the Bottle* and *Hide the Thimble.*[109]

That night when young George, entering into his small brothers' and sisters' pleasure, led the minuet with little Elizabeth Mary Anne Hooe, no one dreamed that he was dancing with his future bride.

Christmas morning, according to custom, nine-year-old John, five-year-old Thomas and that seven-year-old tomboy, Betsy, set off firecrackers under the windows.[110] They were ably assisted by the little negro, Jack, who was Thomas' constant companion. The Cockburns rode over from Springfield for dinner and the Yule log was brought in with much rejoicing and singing. From then on, the tradition was observed of no work for the negroes until the Yule log was consumed. This was a long process, for the darkies always managed to soak it thoroughly in the swamp beforehand, thus to ensure its slow burning.[111]

The party over, the guests gone, and the children sent sleepily to bed, the older members of the family remained by the dining room fire to talk.[112]

George Mason had begged to be allowed to retire from the Committee of Safety but had consented to continue his work on the defense of the Potomac River.[113] Now, in reply to Sarah Brent's question of what ships were available, he told her that Virginia was to build two row-galleys, one to carry a 24-pounder, the other an 18-pounder, and that they were to provide three armed cutters for the protection of the Potomac River.

Sarah looked thoughtfully into the dancing flames and was silent.

Mason leaned forward and studied her face.

"What are you seeing there?" he asked.

Without raising her eyes, Sarah replied thoughtfully, "I see a great navy, as great as the Royal Navy, ships greater than any you or I know—the American Navy, George, is about to be born."

George Mason rose and filled their glasses all round with Gunston Hall's peach brandy.

"The American Navy," he said, and the little circle around the fire arose and drank the toast in silence.

Three days before that Christmas of 1775, a young Scot, John Paul Jones, had been made a lieutenant in the American Navy. This consisted of the *Alfred, Columbus, Andrea Doria, Sebastian Cabot* and *Providence,* the whole mounting 100 guns and manned by 1,150 seamen. Jones was attached to the *Alfred* and was the first to hoist the American flag, thus first displayed on board that vessel.[114]

18

THE FATEFUL YEAR 1776 began with an attack by Lord Dunmore on the town of Norfolk. This unfortunate town had refused to supply his ships with provisions. In retaliation, early on the morning of January 1st, he began a furious cannonading of the town and sent parties of marines and sailors ashore to set fire to the wooden buildings on the water front. It is said that the townsmen themselves destroyed the rest of the flourishing town, so that it might not afford shelter to the royal troops. Thus, the colonies' Year of Decision began, in its early hours, with fire and bloodshed. Ten days later, Thomas Paine published his pamphlet *Common Sense*. It was read throughout the colonies and contributed as much as any one cause to the growing desire for independence. From all sides Mason received news of this growing sentiment. As he had prophesied, the slower minds were catching up with the faster ones. In North Carolina the Mecklenburg Resolves had been adopted, Adams of Massachusetts was now writing his *Thoughts on Government;* and in England, Lord North's efforts at conciliation were beginning to be recognized as too late.

Then, in March, came the news that General Washington's long wait to gather men and supplies had been vindicated. On the 17th, he succeeded in driving the British from Boston. They withdrew to Halifax and Americans wondered where they would strike next.

In the meantime, the Virginia Convention was called to meet in Williamsburg in May. This time, Mason consented to serve and arrived late because of another "smart fit of the gout."

The late "House of Burgesses," or the "Virginia Convention," as it was now called, met in the Capitol at Williamsburg on the 6th of May. This building was not the prototype of the beautiful capitol we know today. That was destroyed by fire in 1747 and was replaced by a brick structure of little beauty. It was there, with Patrick Henry in the speaker's chair, that the 3rd Virginia Convention resolved itself, on the 15th of May, 1776, into a committee on the state of the colony. Colonel Archibald Cary reported the famous Resolutions for proposing independence. These were written by Edmund Pendleton.[115] According to Edmund Randolph, Patrick Henry was selected to make "a movement for independence . . . and stood like a pillar of fire before the Convention."[116]

The Journal of the Convention records that it was "Resolved unanimously that a committee be appointed to prepare a Declaration of Right and such a plan of government as will be most likely to maintain peace and order in this colony and secure substantial and equal liberty to the people."

This action of the Virginia Convention was the first step taken toward the Declaration of Independence of the United Colonies. That night the little town of Williamsburg celebrated the great event with a military parade. The resolutions were read aloud to the troops before the Committee of Safety and the delegates to the Convention. The "Continental Union Flag" was displayed and the town was illuminated. Two days later, appalled at their own courage, they kept a day of fasting and prayer.

While this momentous event was taking place in Williamsburg, the Continental Congress was sitting in Philadelphia. There, on May 10th, John Adams had introduced the resolution recommending to the colonies "where they were left without governments sufficient for their needs, to adopt such as they deemed expedient."

All this had transpired before George Mason, now called Colonel Mason in recognition of his work on the Committee of Safety, arrived in Williamsburg. We can see him walking up the steps of the Capitol on the 18th of May, the morning after his arrival, leaning heavily on his cane, his face showing the marks of suffering and anxiety. His figure was no longer young and graceful. It had thickened with the years but his air of distinction had increased and his courtly charm had not lessened. Thomas Ludwell Lee hastened with others to meet him.

"At last you are here, Colonel," he said. "We are greatly in need of you. The plan must be preserved from becoming in the end a jumble of discordant, unintelligible parts. It demands the protecting hand of a master."[117] He added anxiously, "I wish to Heaven my brother Dick were here."

Mason put his hand affectionately on Mr. Lee's green coat sleeve.

"Perhaps we can persuade him to leave the Congress and come down," he said. "It is a question where he is most needed."[118]

The two gentlemen were joined by John Augustine Washington who gave it as his opinion that the Virginia Resolution was "not so full as some would have wished, but," he added, "I hope (it) may answer the purpose. What gave me pleasure was that the resolve was made by a very full house and without a dissenting voice."[119]

The Committee to prepare a Declaration of Rights and a Constitution for Virginia had been appointed on May 15th. It consisted of twenty-eight members. Madison had been added to the Committee on the 16th, and now, when Colonel Mason took his seat in the Convention, he was put at once upon this important Committee. He was placed upon four other committees on that same day. That evening, back in his room at the Raleigh, we see him at the table in his room, and James, his servant who had replaced his loved Enos, was carrying in a brass pitcher of hot water and laying out his master's clothes for the night. As Mason wrote, the ruffles at his wrist made a little sound passing over the paper. He wrote hastily, reading his pages from time to time. He was writing his old friend Richard Henry Lee.

"The Committee," he wrote, "appointed to prepare a plan is, according to custom, overcharged with useless members . . . We shall, in all probability, have a thousand ridiculous and impracticable proposals . . . This can be prevented only by a few men of integrity and abilities, whose country's interest lies next to their hearts, undertaking this business and defending it ably through every stage of opposition.

"I need not tell you how much you will be wanted here on this occasion . . . It will be some time, I presume, before that assembly (the Congress) can be fully possessed of the sentiments and instructions of the different provinces, which I hope will provide you time to return."

And now looking ahead, Mason paused to consider the dangers and almost insurmountable difficulties that would confront the new little country which was about to declare itself upon its own. He looked thoughtfully out of the window and then resumed his writing.

"Pray confer with some of your ablest friends at Congress upon the subject of foreign alliances; what terms it will be expedient to offer. Nations, like individuals, are governed by their interest. Great Britain will bid against us. Whatever European power takes us by the hand must risk a war with her. We want but two things—a regular supply of military stores, and a naval protection of our trade and coasts."

He spoke of our imports and exports, adding, "It is an important and delicate subject and requires thorough consideration. I know you will excuse my loose thoughts," he wrote . . . In a postscript he added, "You . . . will be best able to judge whether, at this crisis, you can do most service there or here, and I am sure you will act accordingly."[120]

Mr. Richard Henry Lee remained in Philadelphia, where, on the following July 4th, he was among those who signed the Declaration of Independence. In Virginia, at the Convention, "the Committee to Prepare a Constitution" reported, on the 27th of May, that they had prepared a Declaration of Rights and on the 12th of June,[121] with several amendments, it was approved and passed the Convention.

We have George Mason's own word that he wrote the Bill of Rights for Virginia.[122] He also infers that he wrote the Constitution for that colony, which, having declared its independence, was no longer a colony. It must now have its own legislature. It must be organized and equipped for government. To that task the Committee to Prepare a Constitution was now dedicated. It was, in the words of the Convention, "A Declaration of Rights and such a plan of Government as will be most likely to maintain peace and order in this colony, and secure substantial and equal liberty to the people."

With the acceptance by the Convention of the Bill of Rights, the Committee now turned its attention to a plan of government which should make workable the principles of the Bill of Rights. This they called "the future form of the government of Virginia." Of this, we have no original draft in George Mason's writing, but we have Thomas Jefferson's word for it that Mason was the author of Virginia's Constitution, as well as of the Bill of Rights.[123] He said: "The fact is unquestionable that the Bill of Rights and the Constitution of Virginia were drawn originally by George Mason, one of our really great men, and of the first order of greatness."

The Constitution was unanimously adopted on the 29th of June, when Virginia gave to America the first written Constitution of a free state in this hemisphere.[124] From the 18th of May until late in June, Mason had labored early and late, in committee, at informal gatherings at the Raleigh, and alone in his room when others slept, building a plan for government under which man should be able to enjoy "certain inherent natural rights." He believed that "God and Nature" had vested power in the people. In the government he strove to build, there must be justice, moderation, temperance, frugality and virtue, and frequent recurrence to fundamental principles. The duty which we owe our Creator and the manner of discharging it can, he believed, "be directed only by reason and conviction and that all men should enjoy the fullest toleration in the exercise of religion, unless under color of religion, any man disturb the peace, the happiness, or the safety of society." And he added, "that it is the mutual duty of all to practice Christian forbearance, love and charity towards each other."

Under a system of government in which he was ruler of his own domain, he had learned and practiced the fundamental rules governing human peace. It was not by chance that he had a happy plantation and an affectionate and happy family. He was well versed in English Common Law. His thoughts must have returned again and again to that wise Scot who had been his guardian, teacher and friend, Mr. John Mercer of Marlborough. What a blessing that library had been to his boyhood! He, George Mason, would use his influence to prevent anything being taken from the English Common Law,[125] which was one of our greatest heritages. He remembered his mother's insistence that Thomson should study law at the Inner Temple in London, as her father and grandfather had done. Back he went into the history of English Law, the Saxon Charter, Magna Carta, the Cromwellian Constitution, and Sully's Bill of Rights, written for William of Orange.

He reviewed too, the numerous pamphlets and Puritan documents he had studied in his library at home, and the names of Richard Overton, Samuel Rutherford, Henry Parker, Roger Williams, John Lilburne, Anthony Ascham and others brought their wisdom to mind. The words "life, liberty and property" were older than Magna Carta,[126] he remembered. He would change them slightly, for men grew with the years and this new declaration must be the expression of later and more mature thinking. "Life and Liberty and the Means of accruing and possessing Property and Pursuing and obtaining Happiness and Safety." He would put it this way.

English minds of the past had followed the same road he was now travelling. Why, when their history was ours, could they not understand that the glory and hope of this new land was theirs also? Well, perhaps that would come later. Ann had been fond of saying, "Rome was not built in a day," and neither, he supposed, would be the good world he envisaged.

Men, he felt, should be free to worship as their consciences indicated. True, he belonged to the Church of England and had been active in Truro Parish since his youth. But the Church was a living thing! If one tried to crystallize it into one form, one provoked a Protestant Reformation, bloodshed and cruelty. He remembered that the Virginia Church[127] had been tolerant of the Huguenots and of the Presbyterians. The Quakers had not been tolerated, but that was because they had disturbed society, coming to the parish churches and creating a disturbance. That was, of course, long ago, when they were of a new faith and fanatical. Now they were quiet and gentle people and everyone spoke well of them. If a government gives people time, he ruminated, they usually settle their own problems peacefully. There was another religious denomination to be considered also. His friend Robert Carter of Nomini Hall was greatly interested in the Baptists. They were growing rapidly in numbers in Westmoreland County. It was not the prerogative of the government to interfere with these good people. Many of his neighbors across the Potomac were Roman Catholics and he himself was engaged to marry a lady who, although herself a Protestant, came of a family which adhered strongly to the Roman faith. Sarah Brent's family and his had been friends for over a century. Christian forbearance—that was a country's need and should be written into a Bill of Rights.

These were not newly formulated thoughts in George Mason's mind. He had turned them over and over, weighed and sifted them as he tramped the shores of Dogue's Neck, rode to the racecourse or to hounds. On winter evenings in his study he had jotted them down on paper, upon his little writing table. Now they were to become part of Virginia's law.

The next step had been a Constitution for the state and after that Mason had been made Chairman of the Committee to design the great seal for the state.

Virginia's Declaration of Rights and the new Constitution were now taken to Philadelphia to the Continental Congress, where Thomas Jefferson wove the Bill of Rights into the Declaration of Independence, destined to be signed upon the Fourth of July. Eleven years later, both these Virginia documents were used in part, in drawing up the Constitution of the United States of America.

In Williamsburg, however, the delegates continued their work. Now that they had a constitution they must make it work. Patrick Henry had been acting governor after Dunmore's departure. He was elected now constitutionally, and Mason was chairman of the committee that notified him of his election. The Convention now adjourned to reconvene as the first Virginia Assembly the following Autumn.

Mason was free, at last, to mount his horse and ride home to Gunston Hall. He was sure that young George had done his best with the harvest and that he had had all the scythes, cradles and rakes got out in order. Colonel Mason had written full directions for his son to Martin Cockburn.[128] He was not worried, but he would be glad to be home.

19

Home again at Gunston Hall, Colonel Mason found his own family affairs closing about him as a stream closes about a swimmer. Young George was eager to give an accounting of his stewardship of the plantations. Nancy, Sally and Mary wanted his reassurance that their beaux in the Maryland and Virginia armed forces would be unharmed. Thomson's horse had strained his right foreleg—would his father look at it? There were new foxhound pups. John felt sure his father would wish to see them before he did anything else. Actually the matter which arrested Colonel Mason's interest as of primary importance was Nancy's report of Liberty. Her sorrow over Enos' death had been restrained but devastating. Nancy had relieved her of the care of the small children, putting Mulatto Pris,[129] the daughter of Jenny, in her place. She had moved her into the quarters near the great house, the cabin where the beloved Nan Old Gate had lived out her last years. But gentle little Libby grew thinner and thinner, and while the Colonel was away at Williamsburg, she had been quite ill. Nancy was distressed and lifted such a worried and anxious face to her father that, in spite of the seriousness of her news, he paused to draw one of her auburn curls around her neck and to touch her cheek lightly and lovingly as he did so.

"She probably needs someone to take care of. You have been too considerate, honey. We must help her to forget herself. Libby naturally thinks of others," he said.

He went to see her at once and found her sitting on her doorstep, apathetically shelling peas for House Nell. At sight of the Master she rose somewhat uncertainly to her feet, a smile brightening her thin brown face. Her hair was turning gray, as was her Master's. She was no longer the pretty, fawn-like creature he remembered at the Eilbecks' Mattawoman plantation.

"Sit down, Libby," he said, seating himself on a bench by the doorway. "Miss Nancy tells me you have had the misery. What seems to be the trouble?"

Libby's face contracted, partly from emotion, partly from the effort of putting thoughts into words. How could she explain the endless loneliness of her life without Enos?

"I doesn't rightly know, Masta," she said, "but since Enos gone and left us, livin' is so daily."

"I know, Libby," the Colonel replied. "I found that out too. But Miss Nancy couldn't get along without Libby! You know I think Miss Nancy's looking a little pale. Have you noticed it? What do you think is wrong there?'"

"Yes, 'deed I noticed it, Masta. Miss Nancy's eatin' her heart out for dat young ge'men from Maryland. I hope he comes back soon. I shore do!"

"So do I," the Colonel said sadly, "but, in the meantime, we must get the roses back into her cheeks. Try to help me, Libby, won't you? You've always been good with Miss Nancy, ever since she was a little tot."

In the weeks that followed, Nancy wondered what her father had said to Libby. She seemed almost her old cheerful self. When Nancy was downhearted, amazingly it was Libby who cheered her. This was true when, at the very end of August, news came that the British had sailed down from Halifax and appeared in New York Bay. General Washington had marched his men from Massachusetts and a terrible battle was about to be fought in a forest on Brooklyn Heights. The Maryland militia were there as well as some American ships, and Nancy was frozen with fear of the news any hour might bring. Rinaldo's secret mission was undoubtedly there.

"Don' you worry, chile, Libby's beautiful baby Miss Nancy! Everything goin' be all right, honey."

"Oh Libby," Nancy sobbed, throwing her arms around Libby's frail little person, "the outlook is so black, so black!"

"Then honey, you must jes try the uplook," Libby comforted her.

Colonel Mason, hearing this conversation, smiled wisely and knew that Libby had recovered.

In September, news of the Continental Army began to come in. Whatever Rinaldo Johnson's mysterious errand to New York had been, he was safe when he wrote, and on the New Jersey side of the Hudson. This, added to his assurances of devotion, sent the young woman singing about the house as she had done in the past. The part of his letter she permitted the others to see described the gathering of several British fleets in New York's harbor. They assembled, he said, in the lower bay. Admiral Howe, a brother of General Howe, who had commanded the British at Boston, was in command. His ships had carried the besieged British forces from Boston to Halifax and had now brought them to New York for a new attack. He had landed 9,000 veterans on Staten Island on the 9th of July. The troops had been brought ashore with the aid of twenty large hay boats. These belonged to American loyalists, of whom there were many living along the creeks and bays of Long Island.

A few days later, a second British fleet had appeared. It had been repulsed in the siege of Charleston, South Carolina. This fleet carried 3,000 men, commanded by General Sir Henry Clinton. The fleet was commanded by Admiral Sir Peter Parker. It had two fifty-gun ships, five frigates of twenty-eight guns, one of twenty-six and two sloops of eight guns each. The shattered masts and pierced hulls of the squadron bore silent witness to the fierce resistance it had met from the guns of Charleston's Fort Moultrie.

From then on, every day saw more reinforcements arrive. A fleet appeared from off the coast of Florida and vessels from Jamaica. Then came a fleet of tall ships from the Mediterranean.

Johnson had seen them standing up the wide estuary of New York Bay and he had seen six men of war and eighty-two transports, carrying 7,800 Hessian mercenaries and 1,000 English guards, anchored below the Narrows.[130] In addition, he said, there were 800 negroes, collected by the British on Staten Island, and these were to be formed into regiments.[131]

Johnson then commented on the man in command of all these ships, Admiral Sir Richard Howe, and Martin Cockburn, who had come in for a few minutes, felt his eyes fill with tears at the young Marylander's praise of a great Englishman. He was as different, Johnson said, from his brother, General William Howe, as white from black, and he added that he was known to be "a dangerous enemy, a faithful subject to his King and a Christian gentleman."[132] Martin Cockburn, could he have looked ahead to the year 1812, would have seen his own nephew, then Admiral Cockburn, as the Admiral in command of another British fleet which would, unhappily, wage a second war on Britain's blood brothers in America.

Other letters followed from other young men. Mary had a letter from one of her beaux who was in General Smallwood's regiment. The regiment, he said, would go into battle without its general, for Washington had ordered Smallwood to remain in New York for a courtmartial, the trial of a Lieutenant Colonel Zedurtz. The regiment would, consequently, be commanded by Lord Stirling, an American who, before the conflict, had claimed his right to the title. He was an able officer and the seven hundred and fifty Marylanders, who had marched in a body the whole distance from Southern Maryland to New York, were undismayed.

Last of the letters from New York, was one received by young George Mason from a boyhood friend in Maryland. It was dated New York, August 30, 1776.

"I have just time to give you a short account of our late engagement at Long Island. On Tuesday we received intelligence that the enemy had landed their troops about five miles below our lines; in consequence of which, General Stirling was ordered to march to the right and General Parsons to the left, with the Brigades under their commands, to take possession of some rising ground, in order to flank the enemy and retard the march until a sufficient reinforcement should be sent from this place to man the lines.

"We began our march to the right, at three o'clock in the morning, with about thirteen hundred men, and about sunrise, on our near approach to the ground, discovered the enemy making up to it, and in a few minutes our advanced parties began the attack; we immediately advanced, and took possession of the ground and formed the line of battle, when our parties retreated to the main body and formed in line with us. In the meantime they began a warm fire with their Artillery and Light Infantry, from their left, while the main body was forming in columns to attack us in front. Our men behaved well, and maintained their ground, until ten o'clock, when the enemy retreated about two hundred yards and halted, and the firing on each side ceased, at which time we heard Generals Sullivan and Parsons engaged on our left. About eleven an express came to his Lordship, on which one battalion of Riflemen was immediately dispatched to their assistance, which left us with no more than nine hundred and fifty men. We soon heard the fire continue round on our left, and in a short time discovered part of the enemy in our rear, going on to our lines, in order to cut off the communication between us. Being thus surrounded, and no probability of reinforcement, his Lordship ordered me to retreat with the remaining part of our men, and force our way through to our camp. We soon fell in with a party of the enemy, who clubbed their fire locks, and waved their hats to us, as if they meant to surrender as prisoners; but on our advancing to within sixty yards, they presented their pieces and fired, which we returned with so much warmth that they soon quitted their post and retired to a large body that was lying in ambuscade. During this interval, the main part of our force retreated from the left through a marsh, with twenty-three prisoners, and got in safe, with the loss of one man killed and three drowned in crossing the creek. We were then left with only five companies of our battalion, when the enemy returned, and after a warm and close engagement for near ten minutes, our little line became so disordered we were under the necessity of retreating to a piece of woods on our right, where we formed and made a second attack, but being overpowered with numbers, and surrounded on all sides, by at least twenty thousand men, we were drove with much precipitation and confusion. General Stirling on this retreat was missing, whose brave example had encouraged and animated our young soldiers with almost invincible resolution.

"The impracticability of forcing through such a formidable body of troops, rendered it the height of rashness and imprudence to risk the lives of our remaining party in a third attempt, and it became necessary for us to endeavor to effect our escape in the best manner we possibly could. A party immediately retreated to the right through the woods, and Captain Ford and myself, with twenty others, to the left, through a marsh; nine only of whom got safe in. The principal loss sustained in our battalion, fell on Captains Veazey, Adams, Lucas, Ford, and Bowie's companies. The killed, wounded, and missing amount to two hundred and fifty-nine; our whole loss that day supposed to be near one thousand, chief part of whom are prisoners, among whom are Generals Sullivan and Stirling. The above is as circumstantial an account as the hurry and want of time will admit of.

"A list of the killed and missing in the Maryland Battalion: Captain Veazey killed; Lieutenant Butler, said to be killed; Ensign Fernandes, Lieutenant Dent, Captain Bowie, missing; Lieutenant Sterret, Coursey, and Wright, Ensign Ridge, thirteen Sergeants, and two hundred and thirty-five privates."[133]

After this, news and rumors came in increasing volume. General Washington was retreating through New Jersey and the British held New York City and Long Island. It was a winter that tried the souls of men, and many whose enthusiasm had been kindled by the first stirring successes of the Continental

Army, now became discouraged. There were deserters from the army and critical comments in the state assemblies. At Gunston Hall, young George Mason was forced again and again, by recurrent attacks of gout, to give up his military service. Thomson and William grew increasingly restive and were eager to give up their books and be off to the armed forces. On every side Colonel Mason encountered anxiety and dissatisfaction.

20

IN THE MEANTIME, Sally's anxiety was as intense as her sister Nancy's, and less controlled. Young Daniel McCarty, whose father was colonel of a regiment in the Continental Army, was a lieutenant at sixteen and serving under Colonel Grayson, a neighbor of the McCartys and of the Washingtons. In Sally's vivid imagination, he died a thousand deaths. When the news came that he had been brought home, near death with camp fever, Sally's never great self-control vanished completely. It was late one autumn evening in November when Mr. Triplett, traveling from Alexandria to Richmond, stopped for a night at Gunston Hall and brought the unwelcome news. In Alexandria, he had heard of young McCarty's return to his father's home. The excitable little Sally ran weeping to her room and Nancy, who followed more slowly, found her in the great four-poster bed, a tumbled heap of flowered skirt and ruffled petticoats, sobbing hysterically and refusing to listen to her older sister's words of hope and comfort.

"At least," Nancy offered, "he was able to travel and we know he is at home and being cared for lovingly."

Strangled sobs were Sally's only response, and when Nancy put her hand hesitantly on the little sister's shaking shoulders, she found herself violently repulsed and shrank back in dismay. To her relief, their brother George appeared at that moment. He was wearing the severe, older brother's expression they all

feared and his icy tones cut through Sally's uncontrolled weeping.

"Sally," he said sternly, "pull yourself together! I'm ashamed
of you. What would Daniel McCarty think of such a per-
formance? Tomorrow you can ride to Cedar Grove with some
of Father's medicine for the flux—that is, if you haven't made
yourself sicker than Daniel is. In that case you will have to stay
drooping at home—a useless female."

Sally sat up. "What a horrid name—a useless female!" she
said.

Her lip began to tremble again but one look at George's stony
expression stopped a second paroxysm of grief. Nancy stole out
softly, and a few moments later Sally reappeared in the drawing
room on her brother's arm. And if her voice quavered as she
asked for futher details, there was now no threat of hysteria in
her pretty manner.

Mr. Triplett said young McCarty was a very lucky young man
to occasion such concern. He said there had been a great deal of
illness in the American Army and that the Carters at Nomini
Hall were sad over the news that their son's erstwhile tutor,
young Philip Fithian, had died of camp fever after the Battle of
White Plains. He added that young McCarty couldn't be in too
bad shape since he had been able to travel. The good gentleman was obviously distressed to have occasioned such a storm
in the Mason household, and Sally, stealing a glance at her
father's reserved profile, began to feel that she had acted like
a child and not the mature and marriageable young woman
she desired to be.

For her, happier days were ahead. The next day she and her
father rode to the McCartys' place, nearer Mount Vernon, taking
with them the prized and effective medicine for which the
prescription had come from England long before.[134] Young
McCarty recovered quickly and their love affair progressed as
smoothly as was possible when the young lady in the case had
inherited all the vivacity and hotheadedness of her most daring
ancestors. Young Daniel has pursued her with patient devotion

since her babyhood. Never understanding her, he had been dashed at intervals from the gates of heaven to the depths of despair. Then, in uniform and an officer, he had at last almost won her promise—but not quite. It was at this point that he returned home in November 1776, desperately ill and about to retire from military service.[135]

One day when Sally had exasperated him beyond endurance, he resolved not to see her again and went fox hunting instead. The fox led him over field and brook toward Dogue's Neck. At length, with the hounds in full cry and the quarry in sight, he found himself where he least wished, or so he told himself, to be. He was on the Masons' home plantation. The fox slithered under a rail fence and McCarty and his horse rose over it in a graceful leap. There, directly in their path, her yellow curls tumbled, her cheeks crimson and lips parted, stood Sally. McCarty saw the fox, obviously her pet, run to her feet. She stood surrounded by the dogs, defiance personified. McCarty, in pink coat, his tanned face as flushed as her own, drew in his mount with superb horsemanship, dismounted and ran toward her.

"Touch him if you dare!" she said.

"No, my lady," he replied, "it is not the fox I am after but the vixen!"

At a word from their master, his dogs slunk back, mystified but obedient. A moment later, his servant, on an inferior mount, came up with his whip.

"And now come here, my beautiful vixen,"[136] he said.

He stood holding out his arms, his square chin uptilted, his eyes smiling, and Sally ran into his arms where she had wanted to be all along.

Shortly thereafter, there was a wedding at Gunston Hall. Candles were lighted in all the rooms and music floated down from the musicians' gallery at the top of the stair. The bride, with her golden-brown curls, seemed a young Diana, untouchable but alluring. The bridegroom had charm of a kind which later came to be known as American. They were very young,

very handsome, and very happy. They were surrounded that
night by the quality of Chotank, as the Maryland and Virginia
country along the Potomac was then called.[137] It seemed that no
evil thing could touch so fortunate a pair. McCarty would take
his bride to live at beautiful Cedar Grove on Pohick Creek.[138]
It was built upon land surrounded on three sides by the silvery
river. Their children and their children's children would play
many parts in a new world which, like themselves, would be only
a new expression of the old. But it was a new world in which a
golden thread was breaking into new strands. A hope of glory
was, even then, being born anew. Man was taking on a new
dignity and a new value. A clear high note as from a silver
trumpet had come shivering down the ages, and, enriched, was
beginning to swell into a great melody. Faintly, in that moment,
George Mason caught the promise of something great and beautiful ahead. He stood alone upon the lowest stone step of the
porch on the land front. The chariot to carry away the first bride
was at the door. The crowd parted and she was in his arms, all
tears and laughter and an ineffable sweetness compounded of
lavender and Sally herself. And then they were gone, around
the carriage drive and down the avenue of cherry trees. There
behind him were a smiling, weeping host of friends and family
and servants, and young George offering his arm.

21

DURING THE TERRIBLE WINTER of Valley Forge in 1776-77, while Lady Washington shared with her husband the hardships of the Continental Army; when Philadelphia lay in the hands of the British; and Congress met in York, Pennsylvania, old Mr. Brent died peacefully at Woodstock. Sarah had been tied closely to his side, for her sister-in-law, Mrs. Robert Brent, refused to take any responsibility for the old gentleman as long as he had an unmarried daughter able and willing to be his constant attendant. In his chintz-curtained bedroom, Sarah nursed her father and watched the world-shaking events which seemed to touch her own life at no point. Her brother's elder boy had joined the Continental Army,[139] and Sarah knit constantly, making socks for him and for the sons of friends, but she had nothing and no one of her own to give. Her thoughts often wandered to Gunston Hall. George Mason had accepted the status quo. It seemed to Sarah he had accepted it too easily, but she reminded herself that he was no longer a young man and his life was full of many things. His wisdom was constantly drawn upon by Virginians who were in the forefront of the country's affairs. The defense of the Potomac area was his particular concern and responsibility, and the private affairs of each of his children were of paramount importance to him. She could not, Sarah told herself, expect him to be constantly at her doorstep as a young lover would have been.

"If only," she thought, "I needed him less and he needed me more!"

Considering her situation, sometime before her father's death, Sarah wished that Colonel Mason's most recent visit to Woodstock had been occasioned by a desire to see her and not, as she knew to be the case, to talk to her brother about his tobacco crop. There was a ship being loaded at Alexandria with tobacco, he had said, which was to be sent to Europe, there to exchange the tobacco for needed military supplies. Sarah had heard her brother promise all of his present crop for this preeminently important purpose.

At the table and later in the cool garden, Sarah had unobtrusively steered the conversation to Mason's activities. She had learned that cannon were needed to fortify the valuable port of Alexandria. She knew, too, how Mason felt about the "disestablishment of church and state"—that it was unfair for other denominations to be required to support the Anglican church in Virginia. Each denomination, he believed, should be supported by its own members, but "the glebe lands, churches and plate with all arrears of money and tobacco should be secured to the parishes and their incumbents."[140] This would make for hardship for those who, like the Masons, adhered to the Church of England, but it was in keeping with the new national idea of independence and with freedom of worship. Mason had quoted Edmund Randolph as saying that the friends of the old established church thus "cast the establishment at the feet of its enemies."[141]

Sarah had listened gravely, understanding that her greatest value to George Mason, at that time, was as a listener. Talking to her, he had crystallized his own opinions on other problems too—on the disputed boundary line between Virginia and Pennsylvania; on changes into modern English in the English common law, which he desired left intact,[142] and on new statutes, especially the statute of descents. He remembered, he had told Sarah, how bitterly his mother had objected to the law of primogeniture, under which he had received everything, his brother and sister nothing. He recalled how she had purchased, with her own money, large estates for his brother Thomson, in Lowden County, and also land for his sister, Mary Selden. His own lands, he said, would be divided, at his death, among all his sons.

Sarah realized that she could see no more of George Mason than his occasional overnight stops at Woodstock permitted. It was fortunate for her, she thought, that the Brent lands lay between Gunston Hall and Williamsburg, and fortunate, indeed, that in the succeeding assemblies, George Mason was required to serve on so many committees.

Now in this winter of 1777-78, Sarah, who had accepted the dull rhythm of her life as inevitable, found the foundations of her daily existence shaken from beneath her. Old Mr. Brent died peacefully in his sleep, and Sarah awoke to the realization that she no longer was needed nor wanted at Woodstock.

George Mason was in Williamsburg and was again deeply interested in the affairs of the Ohio Company, for George Rogers Clark had walked into the assembly at Williamsburg, demanding the powder stored at Pittsburgh to defend the settlers in Kentucky against the Indians. Clark was told that the ammunition would be lent to Kentucky if they could transport it and pay for it. One hundred and thirty-six kegs of powder had been brought from New Orleans by Lieutenant William Linn, up the Mississippi and Ohio. It was the first cargo transported by white men up those rivers. Clark knew, therefore, that it could be done. The ammunition at Pittsburgh was a necessity, a life-and-death matter to the Kentuckians, but Clark was told he must pay for it and arrange for its transportation. He turned on his heel, saying that a country not worth defending was not worth claiming and that if Virginia would not defend her children, they would look elsewhere.[143]

Without his friend, Colonel Mason, it is doubtful if George Rogers Clark would ever have accomplished the superhuman task for which he is honored today.

After conferences with Patrick Henry, then the Governor of

Virginia, a letter was written on January 3rd, 1778, by George Wythe, George Mason and Thomas Jefferson. These three gentlemen pledged themselves, in case of the success of the expedition, "to exert their influence to obtain from the legislature a bounty of three hundred acres of land for every person in the expedition."[144] Colonel Mason then invited Wythe and Jefferson to meet with him at Gunston Hall to discuss measures for securing the land. Clark returned to Kentucky, and the famous Illinois campaign began. The fight for Detroit and Clark's victory at Vincennes are another story. It was, however, George Mason's belief in the young frontiersmen that made it possible for a band of brave Scotch-Irish to set forth from St. Louis, blessed by a priest and prayed for by Spanish beauties. Long afterwards, George Mason would thrill to the story of the twenty-nine-year-old commander who had led his men across the flooded Wabash country, cheered on through chest-deep ice water by that fourteen-year-old drummer boy, Floyd Isham. The Ohio Company, founded nearly 30 years before, was now about to flower into the states of Ohio, Kentucky, Indiana and Illinois. No wonder George Mason pressed home to Gunston Hall to confer with other members of the Ohio Company.

Later, Sarah would understand, but it was hard, at the moment, to face the future without him. With Little Codger's mournful help, she packed her trunks sadly and prepared to move to Dumfries, there to make her home with her sister, Jane Graham, who always welcomed her gladly. Jane, who really had not been well, insisted that she needed her, and Sarah noticed wistfully that Mrs. Robert Brent only half hid her pleasure when she heard that her husband's sister was going. Rather crisply, she offered her equipage for the short journey but Sarah thanked her and said she would ride her own little roan mare.

This beautiful horse was her one really valuable possession. Colonel Mason had given her the animal when Sarah had admired it as a tiny colt, and he had helped her to break and train it. Sarah never permitted anyone else to ride Winnie and insisted that the little creature and she could read each other's thoughts. Robert Brent agreed to send his sister's negroes,

boxes and horsehair trunks in one of the farm wagons and said
that he would himself escort her to the Grahams' house. They
paused at the gate of Woodstock, while a negro opened it for
them, and Sarah looked back at her childhood home. She
would return many times, but today she was putting a period
mark at the end of a chapter. She studied the familiar lines of
the house as if to fix them in her mind forever: the graceful
roof, the tall pink brick chimneys, the gaunt, friendly oaks, the
two tall, straight holly trees on either side of the door, and the
horse block where her handsome mother had mounted her
spirited horses. Finally, with a sigh that was almost a sob, Sarah
turned her swimming eyes to the road ahead. Robert respected
her silence and they rode some way without speaking. Then
Sarah asked, in a matter of fact voice, "Have you seen or heard
anything lately of Peregrin Fanshaw, Robert?"

Robert's heavy eyebrows drew together at the name.

"Yes," he replied. "No one can prove anything against him
and he is living in Maryland and professing loyalty to the
American cause. He is seldom seen in public and when he does
appear, I am told he talks loudly against the Goodriches and
their depredations to American shipping."

"And where are the Goodriches?" Sarah asked.

"They were down on Currituck Sound," her brother answered. "They captured some boats there, I understand, and
sailed them up to New York to Admiral Howe."[145]

Soon the brother and sister rode into the busy port of Dumfries and Sarah grew silent again, busy with her own thoughts.
At the Grahams' house, old Uncle Ben opened the door.

"Miss Jane taken down sick," he said, his brown face full of
concern.

Sarah ran upstairs and reappeared a moment later, coming
only halfway down. From there she spoke softly to her brother
who started up to meet her. She stopped him with an imperative gesture.

"Dr. Craik is here," she said. "He thinks it is smallpox. You
must go home at once. You can do nothing here. Better not
take a useless risk."

Robert was stunned. "Come back with me, Sally," he begged. But Sarah was adamant.

"No," she said, "I shall stay. I am needed, but you must go. Thank you for coming with me," she added. "I will send you word, when I can, of how it goes here."

It was indeed true that she was needed. One after another the Grahams and some of their negroes came down with the dread disease and one of the negroes died. Sarah was busy night and day and when a violent headache and chill laid her low, she thought her end had come. She recovered, however, and found, to her relief, that her face was unscarred. Weeks had passed since she had seen the outside world and she was so weak she felt that she would never again have the strength to mount and ride Winnie.

Then, one day, she heard the knocker, and a few minutes later a familiar voice in the hall—and Jane's little negress, Nell, ran up the stairs to tell her that Colonel Mason was there.

"Is you able to walk down, Miss Sally?" she asked. "I'll help you." But Little Codger was there first and helped her beloved "Missie" to the foot of the stair.[146]

George Mason was standing in the parlor near the window, with its red brocatelle curtains and deep window seat. In his riding clothes, green coat, riding boots and spurs, his appearance filled the little spinster's very soul with satisfaction.

"Bother," she thought, "why did he come whem I am looking my worst?"

But in Colonel Mason's eyes she was not looking her worst. She was thin and pale but her piquant little face was alight with vivid pleasure and the wistful look in her eyes was increased by the shadows beneath them. Mason held out his arms and she ran into them.

"You didn't answer my letter," he said, "and then I heard you were here in the midst of the epidemic."

"I never received a letter," Sarah replied.

Mason swore softly to himself and drew her down beside him on the window seat. There was much to be said.

"But I wrote you first to Woodstock. Why did you leave there so suddenly?" he asked.

He listened to her account of leaving her old home, only his keen eyes expressing his opinion of her sister-in-law. It was useless to comment. Sarah, he knew, would only defend her.

"And when you reached here you found Jane already down with smallpox?" he asked.

Little by little he pieced together Sarah's saga of quiet heroism and finally her own desperate illness. He took a serious view of the miscarriage of his letters to her. No doubt Mrs. Brent had been afraid to send anyone, after Sarah's departure, from Woodstock to the plague-ridden town, but he had also sent letters directly to Dumfries by the captain of one of the ships picking up military supplies there. This man had promised to see that they were left at Mr. Graham's door. He would look into this and have an explanation. It was unthinkable that Sarah had been without any word from him after her father's death.

She put her thin hand on his and said, "Don't worry. It is behind us. Tell me, instead, about yourself and the children. How is George?"

George, Junior, it seemed, was very miserable. His father was considering sending him to the south of France for a year. Before deciding, however, he would go once more to Augusta Springs. The most important news, at the moment, was of Sally's wedding. Sarah drank in every detail of the wedding she had missed and hoped that Nancy's wedding would follow soon—as would, indeed, be the case.

"And your wedding to me, Sarah," George Mason asked. "When is that to be, my dear?"

Strangely enough, when Sarah heard the words for which her heart had been hungry for years, she was troubled instead of happy, and her hesitation showed in her expressive eyes. She turned them up to Colonel Mason, beside her there on the window seat, and said haltingly, "George, it sounds absurd, after all these years, but the time isn't yet. Nancy must have her wedding with Rinaldo Johnson, just as it is now planned, and little Mary must have the experience of being mistress of your house, for a little time, at least. She has always wanted to do it. For my part, I cannot now leave Jane. I must see her recovered fully from her serious illness before I leave her. When life became intolerable for me at Woodstock, the Grahams took me in. I should ill requite them if I left them now."

She looked down at the square toe of her small red shoe and then up enquiringly at Colonel Mason and, for a minute, her resolve seemed to weaken.

"Oh George," she cried, "am I right? Do you not feel as I do?"

Mason drew her gently into his arms, saying, "For the moment, my dear, you are right—not for the sake of all the other people you are considering, but because you are yourself in need of rest and quiet. We will go on as we are for a little while. But Sally," he added, "you must understand that if I do not see you as often as I should like, it is not lack of inclination on my part but because the times are so pressing. You must not be unhappy when I seem preoccupied. Do you think you can remember this?"

Sarah smiled up at him a trifle uncertainly and moved closer into the circle of his arm.

"It is all very easy," she said, "when you are here, but when I have no news of you, I am tormented with a thousand fears—I wonder if you are ill; if the British have burned Gunston Hall, or if Fanshaw or some other evil person has waylaid you on the road. Oh, I can think of a thousand terrors, but now at this golden moment, I am resolved that I will not."

She drew herself to her full height of less than five feet, standing before him and taking both his hands in hers.

"We will both be sensible," she said, "and when it is right we shall know. Then we will be married and be very, very happy and peaceful for years and years and years!"

Her sudden optimism was contagious and as dazzling as golden sunlight after rain. Mason rose and took her in his arms and neither of them saw Jane Graham's entrance and hasty exit.

22

COLONEL MASON, in his small sitting room, his feet toward the fire on the hearth, allowed his mind to run over the events of the past two years. In the late autumn of 1777, Congress had agreed upon the Articles of Confederation, perpetual union of the new states was agreed upon and the United States of America was given its name. Lafayette and De Kalb had arrived and the promise of France's aid had put new heart into a country struggling to be born into the company of nations. In July, 1778, Count d'Estaing had arrived with a French fleet off the Delaware Capes—a month after Congress had rejected an offer of peace from Great Britain.

At this time George Mason had written to his friend, Richard Henry Lee:

July 21st, 1778
Gunston Hall

Dear Sir:

"I am much obliged to you for the last papers, and the agreeable news they contain. American prospects brighten every day; nothing I think but the speedy arrival of a strong British squadron can save the enemy's fleet and army at New York——."

and again, on August 24th

"We have had such various and vague accounts of our

affairs to the northward and of the movements of the French fleet, that I am extremely anxious to know with certainty what is doing."

Now, on this October evening in 1778, when young George and Nancy had gone over to the Cockburns at Springfield for the evening, Thomson and Mary to their neighbors, the Chichesters, and William was at his studies, Colonel Mason sat down at his writing table near the fire. He called James to bring another candlestand and candle, and after some moving about and looking through packets of letters and papers, settled himself contentedly to write a long letter to a cousin in England. His pen poised above the paper, he sat for a few minutes, looking into the fire. His mind travelled across the Atlantic to London and to his cousin, George Mercer, son of Mr. John Mercer of Marlborough. How many happy days he had spent at their house! George Mercer was younger than he. Mason could even remember his learning to walk. Later, they had all had high hopes for him when he had gone to London as agent for the Ohio Company. Then had come that nightmare affair of the Stamp Act, and young Mercer had come home, actually bringing the stamps with him, all unaware of the storm their arrival would stir up at home. No one had been more irate than his own father, and George Mercer had returned to England. Two years later he had reappeared in his native Virginia, bringing with him an English bride who had lived only for a year. Mercer had gone back to England, and for two years Mason had had no news from him. He welcomed this quiet evening and an opportunity to tell his friend and cousin all the Gunston Hall news.

"My dear Sir:" he wrote in the formal manner of his day, "It gave me great pleasure upon receipt of your favor of the 23rd of April by Mr. Digges, to hear that you are alive and well in a country where you can spend your time agreeably, not having heard a word from you or of you for two years before.

"I am much obliged by the friendly concern you take in my domestic affairs, and in your kind inquiry after my family;

great alterations have happened in it. About four years ago I had the misfortune to lose my wife; to you who knew her and the happy manner in which we lived, I will not attempt to describe my feelings. I was scarce able to bear the first shock; a depression of my spirits and a settled melancholy followed, from which I never expect or desire to recover. I determined to spend the remainder of my days in privacy and retirement with my children, from whose society alone I could expect comfort. Some of these are now grown up to men and women and I have the satisfaction to see them free from vices, good-natured, obliging and dutiful. They all still live with me and remain single except my daughter, Sally, who is lately married to my neighbor, Mr. McCarty's son. My eldest daughter, Nancy, (who is blessed with her mother's amiable disposition) is mistress of my family and manages my little domestic matters with a degree of prudence far above her years. My eldest son, George, engaged early in the American cause and was chosen ensign of the first independent company formed in Virginia, or indeed on the continent. It was commanded by the present General Washington as captain, and consisted entirely of gentlemen. In the year 1775 he was appointed a captain of foot in one of the first minute-regiments raised here, but was soon obliged to exit the service by a violent rheumatic disorder which has followed him ever since, and I believe will force him to try the climate of France or Italy. My other sons have not yet finished their education; as soon as they do, if the war continues, they seem strongly inclined to take an active part.

"In the summer of '75 I was much against my inclination drag'd out of my retirement, by the people of my country, and sent a delegate to the General Convention at Richmond, where I was appointed a member of the first Committee of Safety; and have since, at different times, been chosen a member of the Privy Council, and of the American Congress; but have constantly declined acting in any other public character than that of an independent representative of the people, in the

House of Delegates; where I still remain, from a consciousness of being able to do my country more service there than in any other department; and have ever since, devoted most of my time to public business; to the no small neglect and injury of my private fortune; but if I can only live to see the American Union firmly fixed, and free governments well established in our western world, and can leave to my children but a crust of bread and liberty, I shall die satisfied; and say with the psalmist 'Lord now lettest thou Thy servant depart in peace.' To show you that I have not been an idle spectator of this great contest, and to amuse you with the sentiments of an old friend upon an important subject, I inclose you a copy of the first draught of the Declaration of Rights, just as it was drawn by me, and presented to the Virginia Convention, where it received few alterations; some of them, I think, not for the better; this was *the first thing of the kind* upon the continent, and has been closely imitated by all the other states. There is a remarkable sameness in all the forms of government throughout the American Union, except in the states of South Carolina and Pennsylvania; the first having three branches of legislature, and the last only one; all of the other states have two; this difference has given general disgust, and it is probable an alteration will soon take place, to assimulate these to the Constitutions of the other States. We have laid our new government upon a broad foundation, and have endeavoured to provide the most effectual securities for the essential rights of human nature, both in civil and religious liberty; the people become every day more and more attached to it; and I trust that neither the power of Great Britain, nor the power of hell will be able to prevail against it.

"There never was an idler or a falser notion than that which the British Ministry have imposed upon the nation 'that this great revolution has been the work of a faction, of a junto of ambitious men against the sense of the people of America.' On the contrary, nothing has been done without the approbation of the people, who have indeed outrun their leaders; so that no capital measure hath been adopted, until they called loudly for it: to any one who knows mankind, there needs no greater proof than the cordial manner in which they have cooperated, and the patience and perseverance with which they have struggled under their sufferings; which have been greater than you, at a distance, can conceive, or I describe. Equally false is the assertion that independence was originally designed here: things have gone such lengths, that it is a matter of moonshine to us, whether independence was at first intended, or not; and therefore we may now be believed. The truth is, we have been forced into it, as the only means of self-preservation, to guard our country and posterity from the greatest of all evils, such another infernal government (if it deserves the name of government) as the provinces groaned under, in the latter ages of the Roman Commonwealth. To talk of replacing us in the situation of 1763, as we first asked, is to the last degree absurd, and impossible: they obstinately refused it, while it was in their power, and now, that it is out of their power, they offer it. Can they raise our cities out of their ashes? Can they replace, in ease and affluence, the thousands of families whom they have ruined? Can they restore the husband to the widow, the child to the parent, or the father to the orphan? In a word, can they reanimate the dead? Our country has been made a scene of desolation and blood—enormities and cruelties have been committed here, which not only disgrace the British name, but dishonour the human kind! We can never again trust a people who have thus used us, human nature revolts at the idea! The die is cast—the Rubicon is passed—and a reconciliation with Great Britain, upon the terms of returning to her government is impossible.

"No man was more warmly attach'd to the Hanover Family and the Whig Interest of England than I was, and few men had stronger prejudices in favour of that form of government under which I was born and bred, or a greater aversion to changing it: it was ever my opinion that no good man would wish to try so dangerous an experiment upon any speculative notions whatsoever, without an absolute necessity.

"The ancient poets, in their elegant manner of expression, have made a kind of Being of Necessity, and tell us that the Gods themselves are obliged to yield to her.

"When I was first a Member of the Convention, I exerted myself to prevent a confiscation of the King's Quit-Rents; and altho' I was for putting the country immediately into a state of defence, and preparing for the worst; yet as long as we had any well founded hopes of reconciliation, I opposed, to the utmost of my power, all violent measures, and such as might shut the door to it: but when reconciliation became a lost hope, when unconditional submission, or effectual resistance, were the only alternatives left us, when the last dutiful and humble petition from Congress received no other answer than declaring us rebels, and out of the King's protection, I from that moment look'd forward to a revolution and independence, as the only means of salvation; and will risque the last penny of my fortune, and the last drop of my blood upon the issue: for to imagine that we could resist the efforts of Great Britain, still professing ourselves her subjects, or support a defensive war against a powerful nation, without the reins of government in the hands of America, (whatever our pretended friends in Great Britain may say of it) is too childish and futile an idea to enter into the head of any man of sense. I am not singular in my opinions; these are the sentiments of more than nine-tenths of the best men in America.

"God has been pleased to bless our endeavours, in a just cause, with remarkable success. To us upon the spot, who have seen step by step, the progress of this great contest, who know the defenceless state of America in the beginning, and the numberless difficultys we have had to struggle with, taking a retrospective view of what is passed, we seem to have been treading upon enchanted ground: the case is now altered, American prospects brighten, and appearances are strongly in our favour: the British Ministry must, and will acknowledge us independent states, but (judging of the future by the past) if they act consistently, they will delay this, until mutual injuries and resentments are further agravated, until our growing prejudices against Great Britain are more firmly rooted and until we become better reconciled to foreign manufactures and foreign manners. It will not require many years to accomplish this, and then the wisdom of British councils will sieze the auspicious moment to recognize the independence of America.

"The present plan of the British Ministry seems to be to corrupt and bribe the Congress; but in this, as they have in everything else, they will be disappointed; not that I imagine that there are no rotten members in so numerous a body of men. Among the twelve apostles there was a Judas—but they are too much in the power of the assemblies of their respective states, and so thoroughly amenable to the people, that no man among them, who values his own life, dares to tamper; and upon this rock the safety of America is founded.

"I have thus given you a long and faithful, and I fear you will think a tedious account of the political state of affairs here; my opportunities of knowing them are equal to most men's, and the natural anxiety you must have to be well informed of the situation of your native country, at so important a crisis, we will apologize for the troubles.

"We have had 200,000 acres of land laid off, marked and bounded in one survey for the Ohio (Company)."[147]

At this moment, Mason raised his head, listened intently and wrote a few more sentences. Then he listened again, rose and went toward the front door. A carriage was coming up the drive. He heard it stop and the gate into the house enclosure opened and closed as the carriage approached the house. Sampson, waiting to open the door for Master George and Miss Nancy, was there almost at once beside the Colonel. Puzzled, Colonel Mason recognized the Cockburns' equipage and with a sinking of the heart he saw his son, George, almost fainting as Sampson assisted him from the coach. Nancy sprang lightly out after him, saying:

"George has been taken ill, father—the same thing! He must be put to bed at once!"

Mason was immediately in command.

"He will sleep down here in my room," he ordered. "I will have a cot in my sitting room."

The whole house seemed awake immediately. Maids ran back and forth obeying Nancy's and the Colonel's orders and someone ran down to the boat at the landing, to fetch Dr. Craik. Mason paced up and down the hall when he was not in his son's room. He could hardly bear to look at the boy, whose mouth was set, not to cry out, and his forehead covered with beads of perspiration. Why had he not sent him to the south of France before the winter storms began? The last trip to the Springs had been a mistake and a loss of time—perhaps an irretrievable loss.

However, young George recovered and his father arrived late at the Virginia Assembly. The winter months were enlivened for them all by talk of George Junior's coming trip to France and of the benefits he would, no doubt, receive from a long stay in a land which seemed to Americans of those days, the source of all good and pleasant things.

Colonel Mason asked his friends to give letters of introduction to the young traveller for their acquaintances in France, and during the first week of April, George Mason, fifth, sailed from Alexandria, not to the land from which his forefathers had come, but to sunny southern France, where he remained for the next four years. After he had gone, Colonel Mason received a long letter from General Washington, enclosing letters of introduction for George to present to Mr. Benjamin Franklin and to the Marquis de Lafayette. These, Colonel Mason forwarded to his son. Lafayette had returned to France in January 1779. There he remained for a year, made much of by the King and Queen and lionized by his countrymen. The letter of introduction must have afforded George much pleasure.

The family at Gunston Hall then turned its attention to Nancy's coming wedding with Rinaldo Johnson. He would take her to live at Aquasco in Prince George County in Maryland, and Colonel Mason was unhappily aware that she watched him closely for any signs of sadness of her coming departure. Sarah Brent, still pleading that she was needed at Dumfries, refused to come for any long visit, and Nancy, who had really counted on her quiet, efficient help, was forced to rely on the loved Mrs. Cockburn for advice, and finally, at the last moment, to send a letter to the old governess, Mrs. Newcomb, to come and stay over the wedding.

Mary had already taken over the housekeeping to leave Nancy free to finish the great piles of sewing which now filled her room. Nancy restrained her smiles with difficulty when she heard Mary's exact duplication of her own voice as she gave orders to the servants. Remembering her own miserable struggle to take her mother's place, Nancy was very patient and gentle with her little sister's occasional mistakes. There was no need to remind the child that her father's understanding would never fail her. The boys, too, although they teased her, stood ready to help in any masculine way they could, and Colonel Mason, who was inordinately proud of each of his children, felt Sarah Brent had shown great understanding when she decided to remain absent a little longer and to let Mary have her chance to be the mistress of the house.

The wedding night came at last. The candles were lighted again, and again the drive was full of equipages, the stable with horses, the musicians' gallery with fiddlers and the house with handsome men and beautiful women. Again the marriage service was read in the drawing room, and again a bride in cape and riding hood ran down the steps of Gunston Hall on her husband's arm to ride away from her father and her childhood home. Again Gunston Hall became only the past and prelude to an old, yet ever new, story.

23

THE STABLE at Gunston Hall sprawled beyond the great walnut trees, behind the schoolhouse. It was full of activity in the first week of April in the year 1780. Horses were being groomed, harness rubbed, and the great family coach had been polished till it shown. John, now fourteen, and Tom, ten, leaned side by side against the wall of the carriage house watching Peter, the son of Great Sue and now the head coachman. He was full of importance today, giving directions to stable boys of all ages and sizes. On Monday, he was to drive the coach into Dumfries where, on Tuesday, April 11th, Colonel Mason would marry his second wife, Miss Sarah Brent.

Peter would be the first of the Mason servants to wait on their new mistress. It was especially pleasing to Peter that the valuable little roan mare, Winnie, would return to the Gunston stable. Sarah Brent was well liked, both by the children and by the servants at Gunston Hall, and a pleasurable excitement over the coming quiet wedding had penetrated, not only the great house, but every part of that busy community in which she would be mistress.

The day was warm and sunny, the trees feathery green with April's chartreuse promise of Summer, and the boys, only half aware of the mingled perfumes, breathed the aroma of moist earth mixed with the pleasant stable fragrance. This last was compounded of hay, horses, leather and harness polish and half a dozen other scents too subtle to identify. The great coach was being pushed out on the gravel drive in front of the coach house, there to be given its final perfecting touches.

With a sudden bound, Thomas landed on the step, holding the door handle to steady himself, and rode out triumphantly for fifteen or twenty feet on the drive.

"Masta Tom, you git right off dat coach dis minute!" Peter ordered. "You wanta break yo' neck jas' befo' yo' Pa gonna git married?"

But Tom was already down, scampering happily toward the house, a hound pup, great grandson of old Rion, at his heels. John followed more slowly for he was thoughtful this morning. Tom could not remember their mother but John remembered very well. He remembered the warm, safe feeling of her arms about him, the scent of lavender on her gowns and her joyous, musical laughter. He remembered her illness, too, and how he had loved to clamber up the little bed steps, and sit on her high bed, there to drink some of the delicious rum-flavored milk brought to her every morning. He had been duck shooting with his father the previous winter, and his father had told him of this coming marriage. No one, he had said, could ever take John's mother's place. Mistress Brent, he had explained, would make her own place in all their lives, and he hoped John would help him to make life happy for her. She would not expect any of the children to think of her as their mother, and they were to call her Mrs. Mason. John had scuffed through the coarse meadow grass, now brown and spangled with frost. He had studied his heavy, homemade hunting shoes as he trudged, gun on shoulder, beside his father. A little silence fell between them and he knew he must speak. At last, somewhat jerkily, he brought out, "It'll be all right. She was nice to us all that time—when Mother went. I guess it'll be a bad time for her coming here—at first. It will be our turn . . ."

He stopped. It seemed to him that he had made a long speech. And then his father was holding out his hand, as if to a man, and saying, "Thank you John. You've never disappointed me. I knew you wouldn't now".

Now the time had come. He would keep his promise to his father. In a few days he would ride to Dumfries with the Cockburns, and after the wedding, he and Tom would go to Sally and her husband at Cedar Grove. It was arranged that they would stay there for a week and that Betsy and Mary would go with Nancy and Rinaldo Johnson to Maryland. When they all returned home, they would find the new Mrs. Mason settled at Gunston Hall. Mary, he had no doubt, would be glad to turn over her arduous duties to older and more experienced hands.

John's slow progress had brought him to the porch steps and now, as he mounted them, he noticed the great lion's head knocker, shining brightly after Sampson's recent polishing. The whole house, like the stable, had been in a turmoil of preparation for the new mistress, and John felt it would be a relief to have the period of waiting over and Mrs. Mason settled. She always brought an atmosphere of tranquillity with her. It would be a relief after the weeks of anticipation. It was too bad that George was in France, and Thomson and William in the army, but he felt, with pride, his position as the older of the two sons left at home.

Tuesday, the 11th of April, 1780, found a small gathering at the home of Mr. and Mrs. Graham at Dumfries. Mr. and Mrs. George Mason stood before the fireplace in the drawing room and greeted the members of their families and the few intimate friends who had come to see them married. John felt his father's eyes upon him as his turn approached, and suddenly, words came to his tongue.

"For my brothers and myself, Madam," he said "I give you our welcome".

He was not aware that his smile could have melted a heart of stone and he did not see the quick tears that sprang into Sarah Brent Mason's eyes but he felt his father's warm handclasp and father and son exchanged an understanding look.

A little later, John stood with Tom and the others and watched his father hand Mrs. Mason into the family equipage, climb in after her and ride away with Peter in his blue livery on the box. He noticed tears on Nancy's black lashes and saw Rinaldo Johnson draw her hand through his arm and Libby brush lovingly against her as if to remind her that she, Libby, was here.

Then, suddenly, all was bustle and dear Mrs. Cockburn looking after them all, as she had done for years, and Mr. Cockburn, very English, as he always became in moments of stress, giving numerous orders and getting in Mrs. Cockburn's way till she laughed and everyone relaxed. Sally McCarty collected her two younger brothers and Nancy, her sister. Everyone said good-bye to everyone else and even spiteful Mrs. Robert Brent of Woodstock was being as agreeable as she could. John was soon mounted and ready to ride, with his brother-in-law, Daniel McCarty, beside the coach in which Sally had taken Tom and the Grahams' ten-year-old George. The two ten-year-olds, she knew, would keep each other busy during the week at Cedar Grove.

The following week found them all back at Gunston Hall, and as John had foreseen, Mrs. Mason had already started a beneficent reign. The servants were smiling and peaceful and the quiet house received the influx of its children with no commotion whatever except for happy greetings. Mrs. Mason, with her needlework and gentle manner, seemed, nevertheless, constantly aware of everyone's needs. John and Tom, who now slept in the schoolhouse with their tutor, Mr. David Constable,[148] found their room undisturbed but clean and warm with a blazing fire on the hearth, and Mr. Constable, after a week's hunting, as glad as they to be home.

That night at supper, however, the family being normally large again, the usual little negro boys assisted Sampson in the dining room. They had not been needed when Mr. and Mrs. Mason were alone. It was their duty to receive the dishes of steaming food in the kitchen, to see these were well covered with lid or napkin, and then to run as fast as they could from the outside kitchen, up the steps to the side door, down the long passageway and into the dining room, with the still hot and succulent dinner. Mary, during her short reign as mistress, had been annoyed to discover that small brown fingers sometimes worked quickly in the dark passage. A small boy with a mouthful of delicious wild pheasant had been unable to answer when spoken to and Mary had instituted a now-well-established custom. All the little negroes were required to whistle continuously from kitchen to dining room and tidbits were no longer purloined from the family dinner.[149]

All this was new since Mrs. Mason's last visit and the Colonel had forgotten to warn her, so that when the musical whistling started in the kitchen and grew louder and louder, accompanied by the sound of syncopated shuffling, the lady's brow wrinkled and she looked anxiously at her new husband. He signaled "All's well, don't worry." As the boys entered the dining room the whistling ceased, and under Sampson's eagle eye, the meal was served with perfect decorum. All would have been well if Betsy had not smothered her giggle and choked in doing so. This had set Tom off into such giggling that Mr. Constable had had to reprimand him sharply. Mrs. Mason had become increasingly puzzled, till Mary whispered, "I'll tell you about it after dinner."

After dinner, in the drawing room, with no servants present, Mrs. Mason asked wistfully but with a humorous twinkle, "Now will you please all tell me about our musical dinner?"

And when it was explained she laughed as hard as the others at her own recent perplexity.

Thus, aided by laughter and good will on the part of everyone, time brought a new sense of well being into the household. Sally, at Cedar Grove, and Nancy, at Aquasco, were happy to see their father well cared for, and Mary discovered that her budding romance with John Cooke was ably abetted by a new ally—the new Mistress of Gunston Hall. Tom was made happy by frequent visits from George Graham, and John, who went his own quiet, shy way, saying little but thinking much, was content.

After Nancy's marriage and departure for Aquasco, Libby had drooped noticeably. Nancy, most like her mother, had always been Libby's pride and darling. Without her warm, sweet presence, Libby's world was dark and cheerless so the

Colonel packed her off, across the Potomac to Maryland, with strict instructions to "take care of Miss Nancy."

Perhaps the happiest creature on the plantation, in those days, was Winnie. The little mare had no anxiety about the war and no knowledge of the increasing British depredations along the Potomac. She was back under Peter's care and in her old stall in the stable. Best of all, there were long, happy days with the other horses in the meadow among the buttercups and daisies and the sweet lush grasses.

24

Now, for a while, George Mason dropped out of public affairs. His intermittent attacks of gout made him an uncertain member of the Virginia assembly, and he retired to live the life of a quiet country gentleman. From Gunston Hall he watched with anxiety the progress of events and the trend of men's thoughts.

At Mattawoman, Mrs. Eilbeck lay gravely ill and her son-in-law made frequent trips across the River to see her. The charming house where he had so many associations stirred memories of happy, long-ago days, and as he sat holding the old lady's hand, they talked together of Ann and of the children. William was to inherit his grandfather's house and land. She hoped he would marry sweet Anne Stuart and she liked, she said, to picture them living there with little children growing up where her child had grown to blooming young womanhood. "But," she added, "there will never be another little girl as sweet as mine." To this, Mason gave his fervent assent.

After a moment's silence, Mrs. Eilbeck said: "You were right to remarry, George. Ann would have wished it and I am pleased with Sarah. She is both capable and kind."

George Mason rose and walked toward the window. His hands, clasped behind him, unclasped and clasped again nervously. Before asking Sarah, he had told Mrs. Eilbeck of his intention and she had said the wedding would be wise and suitable. He sought, now, the right words for what he knew was his last comment to Mrs. Eilbeck on his second marriage. At last, he said, "She is, as you say, both capable and kind. What troubles me is that she gives me so deep, so self-forgetful a love that . . ." He turned, holding out his hands with a gesture of helplessness.

Mrs. Eilbeck nodded understandingly, the lace on her cap framing her still pretty face.

"There are some things you must just accept, George," she said. "Accept her love generously and don't try to write a Bill of Rights for women! You know, when the last word is said, we all make our own lives and Sarah is making hers and liking it. Let it go at that."

That December, Mrs. Eilbeck died. Mattawoman went to her beloved grandson, William, some money and negroes to each of the girls, and a young negro boy each to John and to Tom. It was years, however, before William lived there. He was in South Carolina now, commanding a company of 75 volunteers. "Fine young fellows from this county," his father called them, in a letter to George. The conflict in South Carolina was a hard-fought campaign and reached eventually up into Virginia, where Thomas Jefferson's Monticello was threatened by Tarleton's men. News flew from one plantation to another and Martin Cockburn came into Gunston Hall one day with the news that Mrs. Jefferson, who was very ill, had been forced to leave her bed and flee for her life. Not long afterward, the lovely lady's death was attributed to this experience.

When Benedict Arnold's attack on the James River plantations came, Thomson went off on a tour of militia duty there. He also commanded a platoon, as his father wrote George, "in a pretty close action at Williamsburg." It was a golden moment when he came home bringing with him George Rogers Clark, home for a little while and in time to defend Virginia on the James.

As the two young officers cantered down the four miles from the public road, now no longer "the King's Highway," Clark said wistfully, "You had some beautiful sisters, Thomson. All married, I suppose?"

Thomson laughed, "The two oldest ones are married, but there are two more, just as pretty."

Clark seemed not to hear. "Nancy," he said thoughtfully, "whom did she marry?" And when Thomson told him, he was quiet for a while.

Thomson dismounted to unfasten the gate and they rode, under the cherry trees, up to the house. Peter, warned by welcoming whinnies in stable and pasture, came running to see what riders approached. He led away the two tired horses and Thomson mounted the steps with Clark and lifted the great lion's head knocker.

After Kaskaskia and Vincennes and after the last bitter fighting on the James, Gunston Hall seemed another world—a world he had left of his own will, but which he had looked back upon in the hope that it would, one day, be built anew on the frontier.

The welcome the young men received warmed their hearts as the blazing fire warmed their bodies. Colonel Mason could not seem to hear enough of the Ohio country, and Clark wanted his advice on a dozen problems. The Colonel's few congratulatory remarks meant more to him than those of anyone else, and it made him pause when he realized Mason's disapproval of the large sum of his own fortune now invested in this western venture. He reiterated continually, "We must have Detroit. It must be taken!"

"On the James," he said, "Arnold took the very stores promised to me for the taking of Ohio!"

Like a wild caged animal, he rose and paced back and forth in that Virginia drawing room, so remote from the scenes of his own life. The two pretty young women in their flowered and hooped gowns were no more to him than the handsome furnishings of the room. Later, undressing in the chamber Mary and she shared, Betsy remarked upon this with annoyance "all he can think of is Detroit, Detroit, Kaskaskia, Vincennes and Detroit. What a boring man!"

"Tut, Betsy," her older sister reproved her, "you mustn't be so vain. Did you not know what Doctor Franklin said recently to George Clark? He said, 'Young man, you have given an empire to the republic.' "

Betsy tossed her curls. "Well," she said, "Doctor Franklin may like him, but Doctor Franklin and I don't always agree."

Mary laughed, waited for her sister to tumble into the great four-poster bed, and then blew out the candles on the chest of drawers and jumped in beside her.

25

Raiding ships came with increasing frequency, as the terrible year of 1781 wore on into spring, and in April, Colonel Mason learned that Benedict Arnold was at Portsmouth, Virginia. There, under British command, he was busy preparing large numbers of flat-bottomed boats for the purpose of plundering tobacco warehouses and homes along the rivers of Virginia and Maryland.[159] On the third of April, Mason wrote describing this situation, to the Virginia delegates in Congress at Philadelphia. In his letter he said:

"What may be the fatal consequences not only of disabling many thousands from paying their taxes and contributing to the support of the common cause, but of throwing them also as a dead weight on the rest of the community, or how few of them may have public virtue enough to withstand the terrors of poverty and ruin are topics which, however, disagreeable, deserve the most serious reflections that if possible the evil may be averted . . ."

Further on, he continued: "I have mentioned my thoughts upon these very interesting subjects, trusting that the motives upon which I act (the good of our country) will induce you to pardon such a liberty in a private gentleman and render any further apology unnecessary. Ill health hindering my attendance at Richmond upon the last session of the Assembly prevents my knowing which of the Virginia delegates are now in Congress;

otherwise, I should only have written to one or two of the members, instead of addressing myself to the delegates in a letter which from the superscription may appear to have the air of an official one."

American troops, under Lafayette, Steuben and Wayne, now poured into Virginia, and supplying them with provisions became a major problem. They must be provided for but in a manner that would not be too hard on the inhabitants, or formerly loyal Americans might become disloyal overnight. Mason wrote Thomas Jefferson, then Governor of Virginia, telling him that the Commissioners were inflicting needless injury upon the people.

For John and Thomas there were no more pleasant hours of hunting in the marsh or along the shores of the river. Mason considered these places unsafe now for his boys. Instead, they often rode with him to Colchester to see the troops passing through on their way south. There they met the dashing and delightful young Marquis de Lafayette, while one of their father's friends, Mr. Richard Chichester, gave out the quantity of wheat allocated to the Marquis' command. They thrilled with pleasure when they heard their father invite the attractive Frenchman to spend the night at Gunston Hall.[151]

John, who wanted to go into the army, was spellbound in his interest in the preparations for the baggage wagons, cavalry and droves of beef cattle which would take this route. Tom took a typical small boy's interest in everything and, or so it seemed to Colonel Mason, he picked an acquaintance with all the most disreputable characters who came his way. There was one, however, who was unwilling to make friends. He was a grayish, black-bearded man, about Tom's father's age, heavily built and wearing a battered hat pulled low over his face. When Tom discovered him, he was seated on a cask of tobacco outside the grain warehouse. Thomas, bored by his father's conversation with Mr. Chichester, had wandered outside to watch the activities in the little post town of Colchester.

"Where are you from?" Tom asked.

The man gave him a malignant look and told him to run along.
"Would you like to see my knife?" Tom offered.

"Don't want to see nothing," was the discouraging reply. And
then, with a threatening lurch, as if to rise. "Get along with
you!"

Tom got along, but not before he had recognized something
dimly familiar in the vagabond's appearance. Back in the
granary, he found John, who was not greatly interested in his
experience. A few minutes later, however, Colonel Mason, Mr.
Chichester, Mr. Cockburn and the Marquis came out of the
building and John noticed the surly man Tom had described.
The man was watching with close attention, as the four
gentlemen stood talking on the step. Then he noticed John's
clear eyes upon him and turned away hastily, too hastily. The
loose lower lip was hidden under a grey-and-black beard but
the long arms and smoldering black eyes belonged to the man
John had seen again and again in nightmares since the murder
of Enos.

John did not have an opportunity to tell his father what he
had seen and he refrained from speaking of it with his small
brother. The Frenchman's visit was a matter of such importance
and interest that all else was forgotten.

Nevertheless, a few days later, when John and his father were
again riding into Colchester, John remembered and told the
Colonel that, impossible as it seemed, the tramp Tom had tried
to pick up was Mr. Peregrin Fanshaw. Mason reined in his
horse and looked searchingly at the handsome boy riding beside
him. One could trust John. He was not apt to be mistaken.
What had they said, there on the step in the sun, that might be
of value to the enemy? Like Benedict Arnold, Fanshaw was
serving the British and still working hand in glove with the
Goodriches. American ships were now almost nonexistent, due
largely to the Goodriches' raiding—and necessities for Gunston
Hall had become rarities. Neither father nor son could remember
anything harmful that Fanshaw might have overheard.

Their conversation was interrupted by the sound of approaching hoofbeats around the curve behind them. The Colonel, reputedly one of the best shots in Fairfax County, touched his revolver[152] thoughtfully, and then Martin Cockburn rounded the curve.

"I rode after you," he called, as soon as he was near enough to be heard. "There is a British schooner sailing this way and their army is coming too. We are taking everything we can and moving back into the country. You will wish to take Mrs. Mason and the girls to safety. Will you come with us or cross over to Maryland?"

Back at Gunston Hall, the family were electrified by the news and Sarah began at once to give her quiet, intelligent orders. Colonel Mason started a letter to his friend, Pearson Chapman, across the Potomac in Maryland. Mr. Chapman's mother had been a close lifelong friend of Ann Eilbeck Mason.[153] At the same little table upon which, long ago, Mason had written his letter to the merchants of London, he now wrote,[154]

> "Gunston Hall, Thursday afternoon
> May 31st, 1781

"Dear Sir:

"The rapid march of the enemy obliges me to send as many of my effects as I can readily remove, to Maryland, and I expect to follow immediately with Mrs. Mason and my daughters. I must therefore beg the favor of you to permit all the things I send to be put into your dwelling house, for safety, until I can carry them up to my son William's house, at the head of Mattawoman (Creek), which I shall do with all possible expedition. I expect Mrs. Mason and the girls will be over early tomorrow.

"Part of the Virginia Lighthorse crossed at Fredericks (burg?) on Tuesday night; the Marquis' troops (who are not strong enough for an action) were expected there last night, unless prevented by the enemy. Lord Cornwallis, with the main body of the British army, was at Hanover Court House (scarce fifty miles from Fredericks-burg) on Tuesday morning, their object, no doubt, to defeat the Marquis' troops before General Wayne came up, or to prevent the junction: this intelligence comes from an officer sent express to General Wayne and may be relied on. I think if the winds permit, we may expect their fleet up this river in a very few days. Our situation in Virginia is truly critical and dangerous; a very few weeks, unless the enemy can be checked, will place Maryland in the same predicament. Nothing can speedily extricate the two states but the arrival of a strong French fleet which there is reason to expect every day. I have given you the earliest information in my power, that you may endeavour to secure your moveables by carrying them a few miles from the river, where I think they will be safe for some time.

"I beg the favour of you to let your people and cart assist my people in carrying up the things from the landing to the house that the boat may return as quick as possible; and am dear sir

Your most obedient servant,
George Mason"

On the outside he wrote: "If Mr. Chapman is from home, Mrs. Chapman will be pleased to open this letter."

Mr. Pearson Chapman[155]
Charles County
Maryland

John, feeling himself a grown man, went with this first boatload to Mr. Chapman's and Colonel Mason hastened to the houses beyond the stables. There lived his white workmen, cobblers, tailors, weavers, etc., and indentured servants. Some wished to accompany the family, others preferred to remain.

The following morning found the Mason family disembarking from the sailboat at Mr. Chapman's landing on the Maryland side. It was almost directly opposite Gunston Hall. Young Mr. Chapman and his mother were on the landing, awaiting them, and Sarah, Mary and Betsy, their arms full of treasures, were glad that Mrs. Chapman's chariot had driven down to meet them. Colonel Mason and the boys stayed on the landing with Mr. Chapman to see the last of the boxes lifted from the boat into the farm cart. Tom had his hound pup, Di, with him and John, at the last moment, had asked Betsy to bring his mocking-bird in a wicker cage. He had caught and tamed it himself and it was unthinkable to leave it behind.

John was at that stage when he was a child one moment and a man the next. He was now all interest in his father's and Mr. Chapman's conversation. The two men and the boy stood on the wooden landing. Tom and the pup ran back and forth on the dock. An indentured servant and Sampson were making the boat fast and furling the sails. From time to time, Mason peered anxiously down the Potomac, dreading the sails he might see. He and Chapman talked in low voices while the river lapped gently at the piles under the landing.

"If only the French fleet will come soon!" the Colonel said.

"The French ships from Newport didn't help us much in the Chesapeake last month," Chapman commented sadly.

"We hear so much," Mason answered, "one hardly knows what to believe, but we are promised a really strong French fleet soon and that would alter everything."

The boat was now secured and battened down for the night and the Colonel and his host turned and walked to house, followed by the two boys.

After nightfall, when the ladies had retired, Mason stood up and said:

"John, I think I will walk back to the landing and make sure the boat is secure. Will you come with me?"

As he spoke he took up his flintlock revolver which he had placed on the table near him. John rose with alacrity to accompany him and father and son walked silently together down the path to the landing. Their way was bordered with great English box bushes, brought as cuttings from England. As they neared the water there were holly and deerberry bushes and it was between some of these that Colonel Mason saw a light close to

the water's edge. John saw it at the same moment. It flickered
and then appeared to have been extinguished. Thinking it to be
one of the Chapman servants, Mason called, "Who goes
there?"

In answer, a shot rang out and a bullet whistled through a
deerberry bush, burying itself in the branch of a great holly tree
behind them. Immediately, George Mason answered the shot,
aiming at the place where he had seen the light. There was a
crash, as of a heavy body falling and twigs breaking, quite near
them. Groans followed and an oath. Then Sampson called from
near the house.

"Colonel Mason? Dat you? Is yo' all right?"

"I'm all right, Sampson. Bring a lantern and some of the
men and come down here."

But others were gathering rapidly with guns and lanterns
and sticks. A little crowd appeared and Pearson Chapman came
running from the house to find out what was amiss. The Masons
had approached their fallen foe and the Colonel, aided by John,
was examining the wound when the others came up. It was
Peregrin Fanshaw who lay at their feet, bleeding to death from
a wound in his back. He had fired and run, and the ball from
Mason's flintlock had entered his lung. Chapman came up
in time to hear him say:

"You son of the devil, Mason! You've done for me. You
married the two women I wanted and even took my mulatto
wench. But I killed your man, Enos. You didn't go scot free!
Now you've done me in. You've won in the end!"

"I didn't intend to kill you," Mason answered. "I fired because
I was fired upon. Come, let these fellows carry you up to the
house."

As he spoke, waves lapped more heavily on the shore and an
exclamation from John turned everyone's eyes to the river.
There, like ghost ships, rode six schooners, their sails set to
the south wind. The enemy ships were on their way to Alexandria and in quest of the slim American stores of ammunition
known to be there.

When he spoke again, Colonel Mason's voice was a growl of anger, "So that is what you were doing? Signalling the enemy?"

"Yes," the dying man answered, "and on their return, they will burn Mount Vernon and Gunston Hall. And you will ..."[156]

The sentence went unfinished. A great foam of blood closed his mouth to words. The crowd parted and Sarah appeared and stood watching with the others as Fanshaw breathed his last.

But Mount Vernon and Gunston Hall were not fated to be burned that night nor on any other. Colonel Fitzgerald made such a bold show that the British did not land and, although Fairfax County remained the "scene of war" a little longer, the Masons suffered no loss from enemy attack.

In the meantime, the British Commander in Chief, General Clinton, ordered Cornwallis to entrench himself in a strong position which would control a fleet anchorage. Cornwallis selected Yorktown and there took his stand during the last week of August.

26

THE MASON FAMILY returned to Gunston Hall with mingled emotions. They were thankful that the enemy had been driven off, and glad to restore household treasures to their proper places, but the move now seemed to have been unnecessary and there had been some breakage of valued things.

The colonel wrote to George, in France. His letter would be taken by a friend to the Northern States, from thence to the West Indies and there dispatched to France. He wrote:

"I shall write duplicates and direct them to be sent by different vessels. Some of them will probably reach you . . ."

He told George of Mrs. Eilbeck's death and said that George's own estate, which lay near Gunston Hall, was in good order and a promising harvest coming on "if we are able to reap it." He continued:

"This family has not yet lost any tobacco, slaves or other property by the enemy, although their ships have been as high as Alexandria, but we are in daily expectation of sharing the same fate with our neighbors . . ."

The colonel enclosed two letters, as he expressed it, "under the same cover." The second was upon public affairs and ended with the words:

"God bless you, my dear child! and grant that we may

again meet in your native country as free men, otherwise, that we never see each other more is the prayer of

Your affectionate father

G. Mason[157]

In September, General Washington returned to Mount Vernon after an absence of six years. The French fleet had sailed from Toulon on the 15th of April and now, in early September, under the command of Admiral de Grasse, it sailed into Chesapeake Bay. Washington led the British to believe that he would attack them in New York. Instead, he turned down to Virginia where Lafayette was already harrying Cornwallis, striking and parrying like a fencer because his troops were not numerous nor strong enough for open action.

Count Rochambeau and the Chevalier de Chastelleux came from Baltimore to join Washington at Mount Vernon. There Chastelleux was enchanted with the Mount Vernon humming-birds.[158] Colonel and Mrs. Mason and other neighbors dined with the General and Lady Washington,[159] and John and Tom, with their tutor, Mr. Constable, went down to the Old Plantation to watch the boats of every kind and description which were transporting troops and supplies down the Potomac to join a vastly larger number of others sailing down the Chesapeake from the Head of Elk (River) in Maryland. They knew that, out on the public road, supply wagons, draft horses and beef cattle were still rumbling along.

A few days before, Peter had been sent with the family chariot to Mount Vernon, there to take Rochambeau, Chastelleux or any of the other officers from Mount Vernon to Dumfries. This had been done at General Washington's request, and he had arranged that other gentlemen's equipages would take his guests from Dumfries to another town on their way to Yorktown.[160] The Mason boys had wanted to go with Peter. Now they stood on the grassy bank of the river and longed to go with the boats and to take part in the coming battle. It was the eleventh of September, and within the next month, on October ninth, the French and Americans opened fire on the British at Yorktown. On the 19th of October, Cornwallis surrendered with seven thousand men.

The outer perimeter of the whirlpool whose center was Yorktown was far from Virginia. On the North Sea, England was
fighting Holland. The whirlpool included Spain, where Vergennes was trying vainly to please his Spanish allies, as well as
the United States. In the West it touched the Mississippi, now
demanded by America, and the fisheries off the Canadian coast,
also demanded by the newborn country, were now sucked into
the vortex of war. As in the Seven Years' War, which started
upon the western borders of Virginia and was fought out in
Flanders, the effects of the American Revolution were not
localized in the thirteen new states but were part of a great
world disturbance.

After the battle of Yorktown, peace was long in coming.
Finally, a definitive treaty of peace was signed at Paris in 1783
by Great Britain and the United States. Then followed the so-
called Critical Period of United States history, when the Articles
of Confederation served as a fragile cord to hold the country
together. This continued until the signing of the Constitution in
1787.

During these years, life at Gunston Hall did not stand still.
The year the peace was signed in Paris, young George returned
from France and married sixteen-year-old Elizabeth Mary Anne
Barnes Hooe, daughter of Gerrard Hooe. They settled on his
estate of Lexington. This was near Gunston Hall and was given
its name in honor of the battle which touched off the Revolu-
tionary War. William, as his grandmother Eilbeck had hoped,
married sweet Ann Stuart, daughter of the Reverend William
Stuart of King George County, Virginia. They lived in the
Eilbeck house on Mattawassan Creek in Maryland. Thomson
married Sarah Chichester and they named their house, the building of which occasioned Colonel Mason great interest and
pleasure, Hollin Hall, for Hollin Hall in Yorkshire, England.
It was from there that the Thomson family had come, and even
after a bitter and devastating war, England was still "home" to this
English breed of men. Mary was to marry John Cooke, son of

Colonel Cooke of Stafford County, near the land where the first George Mason had settled upon his arrival in Virginia. During these years Betsy, too, fell in love, after breaking many hearts, and became engaged to William Thornton. John and Thomas still remained unmarried in 1787. Thomas was then seventeen years old and John, who was twenty-one, was to go to France the following year. Nancy already had several children and Sally, about whom John said later that he never remembered her saying an unkind word, had lost one of her babies in 1785. Her father's letter at that time reveals his own way of meeting sorrow. He wrote:

"Gunston Hall, February 10, 1785

"My dear child:

"I most sincerely condole with you for the loss of your dear little girl, but it is our duty to submit with all the resignation human nature is capable of, to the dispensation of Divine Providence which bestows upon us our blessings, and consequently has a right to take them away. A few years' experience will convince us that those things which, at the time they happened, we regarded as our greatest misfortunes, have proved our greatest blessings. Of this awful truth no person has lived to my age without seeing abundant proof. Your dear baby has died innocent and blameless, and has been called away by an all-wise and merciful Creator, most probably from a life of misery and misfortune, and most certainly to one of happiness and bliss.

"Your sisters are both at Col. Blackburn's[161] and not expected home before Sunday or you should immediately have their company. Your brother George and his wife are in Chotank. I wish you could come to Gunston Hall. In the meantime I would by all means advise you to lose a little blood without delay, and to take two or three times a day twenty or thirty drops of spirits of lavendar of which I send you some by the bearer. I am

"Your affectionate father
"George Mason

"P.S. Mrs. Mason says your sisters told her they should go
to Col. Cooke's[162] and would not be at home before the
middle of next week. She begs that you will come to
Gunston Hall."

In this same year, George Mason lost his brother Thomson,
of Raspberry Plain, Loudoun County, Virginia. This was a
severe blow, for the tie between the brothers had been very
strong.

The previous year, the colonel had refused to serve in the
Assembly and had been indignant on discovering a plan to
force him to re-enter the Legislature. Now, however, several
matters, close to his heart, came up for decision.

One was the cession of their claims, by those states which
owned western land. The struggle was precipitated by Maryland's refusal to ratify the Articles of Confederation unless such
cessions were made. Another problem was the economic situation
created by the different states' experiments with paper money.
Still another coming problem, which already threw its shadow
across this time, was governmental provision for the Northwest
Territory—that country opened to the states by George Rogers
Clark's gallant fight on and beyond the Ohio. And there would
be still another question there too—slavery was not to be permitted in that Territory. How could the country be half slave
and half free? There were many puzzles that seemed insoluble
and the Colonel talked them over and over with Sarah, glad of
her interest and lucid answers and most glad of her comforting
companionship now that a house once so full of life was growing
increasingly silent.

Sarah, for her part, wore becomingly the new dignity of
Mistress of Gunston. With the children, she was never intrusive
but always available and they turned to her with increasing
frequency. The house ran smoothly and with no apparent effort
and Mason's usually scattered papers now seemed always in order.
Yes, she had brought peace and contentment and her husband
was feeling more fit than he had in a long time.

27

THESE WERE THE YEARS of the Articles of Confederation, and the country was generally considered to be, not actually a nation, but a confederation of states. The states had stood together for a common cause but were now beginning to consider their own particular interests and to resent all encroachments upon their rights. Congress' gravest problem, therefore, had become a general dissatisfaction with the Articles of Confederation.

In 1783, Thomas Jefferson was the head of the Virginia delegation to Congress, which was meeting at Annapolis. Madison was in Annapolis also, as a Virginia delegate, and the two friends had taken a house together. Jefferson had recently lost his wife and, when Congress adjourned, he would sail for France, taking his two older daughters with him. In France, he was to assist Doctor Franklin, who was then our Minister to that country. Later, he would himself be United States' Minister to France. When the friends parted, Madison would return home to Virginia. Now they sat at their supper table. The setting sun threw its rosy light through the small-paned windows and over them both, picking out the hazel flecks in Jefferson's gray eyes and accenting the lines around Madison's mouth.

Land ordinances had become a pressing and baffling problem for Congress to solve, and the two Virginians were concerned over the interests of their own state. Maryland had called upon the states to cede their claims upon land not within their own

boundaries, and Virginia had been the first to comply, giving up
her rights in the Northwest Territory. Congress had not been
empowered under the Articles of Confederation to rule any territory. Many details of imperative importance must be worked
out, and changes in the Virginia Constitution would be necessary.
The two men whose opinions they were most anxious to know
were George Mason and Patrick Henry. Jefferson felt that
Henry's opinions were not always thoroughly considered and
that they might endanger the desirable changes in Virginia's
Constitution, backed as they would be by his flaming oratory.
He felt the need of Mason's clear thinking and dependability.
He talked it over with Madison, knowing that when he had sailed
for France, Madison must settle this matter alone. With his chair
pushed back, his tall body relaxed and knees crossed, he spoke
with his usual quiet assurance. Madison, his small alert person
on fire with interest and enthusiasm, leaned on the mahogany
table. His spirit seemed to burn in his light gray eyes and great
leadership was concentrated in his small frame.

"Your route home," Jefferson said, "lies near Gunston Hall.
Stop for a night and talk with our friend, George Mason. Will
he serve in the Virginia Assembly and what will be his position?
Write and tell me all the things I shall want so much to hear.
Mason and I," he added, "usually agree, though he does not
always go with me all the way."[163]

It was a complex problem that confronted the patriots of that
age, who asked themselves "whether societies of men are really
capable or not of establishing good government from reflection
and choice, or whether they are forever destined to depend for
their political constitutions on accident and force."[164]

Soon after this conversation, George Mason received a call
from James Madison. In the sequence of events to follow, they
both would serve in framing the Constitution, and together, they
would compose the oath of office for future presidents. Madison
wrote to Jefferson after this visit:

"Much will depend on the politics of Mr. Henry which

are wholly unknown to me. Should they be adverse and G. Mason not in the Assembly, hazardous as delay is, the experiment must be put off to a more auspicious conjunction."[165]

Obviously the matter would take time, and there would be innumerable other problems besides the government of new territories to be decided.

Mason, still unwilling or unable to serve in the Assembly, did consent in 1784 to serve on a committee which concerned itself with navigation on the Potomac. He also served as Presiding Justice of the Fairfax County Court at Alexandria, and a matter of deep concern at this time was the support of the clergy of the Anglican Church in the various parishes. State support of the churches was now withdrawn and this was causing real hardship to the clergymen. John Page wrote to Jefferson in 1785 saying:

"We have endeavored eight years in vain to support the rational sects by voluntary contributions."[166]

By rational sects, he meant the old established church to which Mason belonged, but George Mason felt strongly that freedom of religion, and with it freedom to support the church of a man's choice, was the right procedure under democratic government. He was ready to be among those penalized, if only his ideal of government could be realized.

Another pressing problem was the currency. On the 9th of November, 1785, Mason wrote to George Washington:

"Dear Sir:

"The bearer waits on you with a side of venison (the first we have killed this season), which I beg your acceptance of.

"I have heard nothing from the Assembly except vague reports of their being resolved to issue a paper currency; upon what principles or funds I know not; perhaps upon the old threadbare security of pledging solemnly the public credit. I believe such an experiment would prove similar to old vulgar[167] adage of carrying a horse to the water. They may pass a law to issue it, but twenty laws will not make people receive it.

"I intended to go down to Richmond about the fifteenth of the month to have reported the compact with the Maryland Commissioners, (this was concerned with navigation on the Potomac[168]) but I have lately had so severe a fit of the convulsive colic, or the gout, in my stomach, that I dare not venture far from home; it held me from Sunday evening till Tuesday morning, and has left me so weak that I am hardly able to walk across the floor.

"We hope to hear that you, your lady, and family are well; to whom Mrs. Mason and the family here present their best compliments, with those of, dear sir,

"Your affectionate & obedient servant

"G. Mason"

Mason sent his report to the Assembly by letter, for Sarah refused to hear of his going to Richmond, and so it happened that, in spite of his absence, his words opened a series of discussions which led from local problems to greater ones and, eventually, to that Mount Vernon conference which proved the first step toward a new federal government—Mason's report on the navigation agreement between Virginia and Maryland was referred to the Committee on Commerce in the Virginia Assembly. The next step was a compact for the jurisdiction of Chesapeake Bay: its falls, fisheries, lighthouses, buoys, etc. Washington suggested that the committee meet at Mount Vernon. He had dropped in on their meeting at Alexandria and found several members absent. By gathering them as guests at his home he had not only insured their presence, but managed to keep in touch with the decisions of a committee of which he was not a member, and which was better represented in numbers from Maryland than from Virginia. However, it was Mason who drew up the paper which is called "The Mount Vernon Compact".[169] It was only an agreement between two states but it was the nucleus of the coming agreement between all the states which would be the Constitution of the United States of America.

The next step was the Annapolis Convention of 1786. Here it was unanimously recommended that a convention representing all the states, be held at Philadelphia the following May, "to devise such provisions as shall appear to them necessary to render the Constitution of the Federal Government adequate to the exigencies of the Union, and to report . . . to the United States in Congress assembled."

The accomplishment of the Annapolis Convention which came to very little, was largely the work of Alexander Hamilton, a rising young man and a strong Federalist. Mason, who was fearful of a strong central government and viewed with alarm any tightening of the bonds of union between the states was absent. Patrick Henry and Richard Henry Lee were of the same opinion as Mason. Virginia, the Old Dominion, had been to these men, as to their fathers, their native land. Now they were asked to include unknown lands and unsurveyed territories in their patriotism. In short, Mason and his sympathizers felt the country should move slowly, examining each move with care and thoroughness. Washington, Madison, and also the company of Federalists were anxious to strengthen the central government as soon as possible, lest it disintegrate entirely and leave the country in a state of confusion. These were the two points of view to be settled at the Convention. Mason felt that undue haste would lead later to greater trouble, as it did.

Of all the states, Virginia was the first to select her commissioners to the Constitutional Convention. They were to be Washington, Patrick Henry (who declined to serve), Edmund Randolph, John Blair, James Madison, George Wythe and James McClurg, in Henry's place. Virginia's destiny would be in their hands.

28

SHORTLY BEFORE THE DAY set for the opening of the Convention in Philadelphia, General Washington rode in to Gunston Hall. Sarah, who was in the Colonel's little sittingroom at the moment, recognized his tall form as he rode under the cherry trees toward the house. Loving horses as she did, Sarah would have known the tall white horse anywhere as quickly as the tall man who rode him. She tugged quickly at the bellpull that hung beside the door into the hall, and Sampson, in response to her summons, arrived promptly. He opened the door just as the General drew rein by the steps. Washington's grave face lighted with his friendly smile as Sampson appeared and one of the stable boys came running across the grass behind the schoolhouse.

Sarah greeted their unexpected visitor with her usual quiet warmth, and, as the General bowed over her hand, she felt again the sense of security his presence always gave her. The Colonel was soon found, and he greeted his neighbor with un-disguised pleasure. Since Washington's return, there had been much going back and forth between Mount Vernon and Gunston Hall,[170] and Mrs. Mason expressed her regret that the General had not brought his lady with him. He explained that he was on his way from Kenmore, his sister's home in Fredericksburg, and that although he would gladly stay for supper, he must continue his journey afterward. The two men followed Sarah into the drawing room. Their conversation turned immediately to the coming Convention, and after supper, again in the drawing room, and sipping a last glass of Madeira before his departure, the General returned to one of the coming decisions, which seemed to him of primary importance:

"On this Committee, George," he said, "in which you helped so ably to decide the Virginia and Maryland navigation rights on the Potomac, you had a foretaste of the interstate tariff decisions to be made between all the thirteen states. Surely, my friend, it must be apparent to you that without a strong central government, we would be lost?"

The two men were alone, for Sarah had vanished upon some domestic errand. Washington turned his kindly blue eyes searchingly to his old friend, and Mason noticed the lines around his eyes and mouth where anxiety and hardship had left their indelible marks. He had been Commander in Chief of men from all the states. From all of them he had seen young men flock to his Continental Army, and he had come to think in terms of a continent, rather than a state.

Mason, the Virginian, thought in terms of the Old Dominion. He aspired to the highest achievement, whether in private life or in government. He was fearful of cheapening or debasing the new, American ideal of government. Philosopher and lawmaker, his dreams far outdistanced the average conceptions of his day. His superb Virginia must not be forced into a common mould; its gift to the world must not be snuffed out. He leaned forward and tried to put his feelings into words. His handsome, aquiline profile was alive with his intense interest in his subject:

"The revolt from Great Britain and the formation of our new governments at that time," he said, "were nothing, compared to the great business now before us; there was then a certain degree of enthusiasm, which inspired and supported the mind; but to view, through the calm, sedate medium of reason, the influence which the establishment now proposed may have upon the happiness or misery of millions yet unborn, is an object of such magnitude as absorbs, and in a manner, suspends the operations of the human understanding.[171]

"Do, by all means," he said, "let us establish a national government, but never agree to abolish the state governments, or render them absolutely insignificant."[172]

Washington raised his large, well-formed hand at this point. "I think we agree perfectly," he said, rising. But Mason had not finished.

"There are two other problems," he said, "which must be solved at Philadelphia—the states will need a Bill of Rights, and a date must be set in the future when slavery must cease to exist. A Bill of Rights," he said, "should be the preface of the Constitution,[173] and slavery," he added, "weakens the states and is diabolical in itself and disgraceful to mankind."[174]

"True, true," General Washington replied. "There is no disagreement between us, George, except, perhaps, that I feel more strongly than you the need of haste. If the states fall apart, each seeking its own interests, none of our ideals will be realized. United, however, all your wise conceptions can eventually become realities."

What more he might have said, remained unspoken. Mason was standing before the fire; Washington faced him, and from his great height looked across at the painting of Ann, framed in the paneling of the chimney breast. Washington's face softened and relaxed as he looked at Hesselius' effort to transfer Ann's loveliness to canvas.

"Ah," he said, softly, more to himself than to the Colonel. "How sweet she was!"

For a moment both men stood looking at the likeness of a seventeen-year-old Ann. George Mason was sixty-two now; George Washington, fifty-five.

"At eighteen," Washington said, "I considered my heart broken because she married you.[175] No artist," he added, "could ever catch the freshness of her complexion nor the sweetness of her smile."

Mason bowed but did not trust himself to speak, and both men turned toward the hall where Sarah's voice was heard greeting Betsy. A party of young people were just returning from Cedar Grove, and Sarah was saying:

"Betsy, my dear child! I am so glad you are home, for I expected you earlier and was becoming anxious."

Seeing the Masons' distinguished guest, the little group of young men and women became silent, greeted the General with respect and shared in the good-byes. Washington took Betsy's hand in farewell and looking from her pretty, rosy face to her father, he said:

"Miss Betsy, you carry me back forty years, and it is with a poignant pleasure that I, a white-haired man, see in you your mother as a girl. It is not only your mother and you yourself that I behold, but other American girls in years to come, cast in the same mold of noble beauty. God bless you, my dear, and the American woman of tomorrow, too!"

He was gone—a tall man on a great white horse. Horse and rider vanished down the avenue of cherry trees, which were white with blossoms under a spring moon.

29

ALL WAS ACTIVITY IN May, 1787, at the Indian Queen, the fashionable tavern of Philadelphia, Capital City of the United States. Delegates from every state in the Union were assembling for the great Federal Convention, when the government would take on form, reality and power. The Convention would meet within closed doors in the building now known as Independence Hall. The eyes of the world were upon that white paneled, tall-windowed room where, in 1776, the Declaration of Independence had been drawn up and signed. Now another great document was to be written there while the world watched with every emotion from cold cynicism to the highest hope.

At the Indian Queen there was sumptuous comfort, for here a proud city entertained its honored guests.

True, General Washington was the guest of Mr. Robert Morris, and Mr. Gerry had taken a house, so that his young wife and baby could be with him. Not all the delegates were at the Indian Queen, but the guests there numbered among them such distinguished visitors as George Mason and James Madison from Virginia, Rutledge and Charles Pinckney of South Carolina, Governor Alexander Martin and Hugh Williamson of North Carolina, Richard Bassett of Delaware, Alexander Hamilton of New York, Nathaniel Gorham and Caleb Strong of Massachusetts, and George Mason had brought his son John with him.[176] There were others also but their names are not recorded.

These gentlemen, in the colorful dress of their day, and waited upon by liveried servants, thronged in and out of the Indian Queen from the latter part of May until the 17th of September. The delegates arrived slowly, for travelling was difficult, and many of them had far to come. Those were not days of haste or impatience, however, and the earlier arrivals made use of their time by meeting and discussing the grave matters before them.

Colonel Mason and John travelled to Philadelphia by way of Baltimore where he wrote letters to William and Thomson. He and John arrived at the Indian Queen the 17th of May and on the 20th he wrote a long letter[177] to George saying:

"The expectations and hopes of all the Union centre in this Convention. God grant that we may be able to concert effectual means of preserving our country from the evils which threaten us."

He continued, saying that the Virginia deputies met for two or three hours every day and there was a general meeting of all the deputies who had arrived, every afternoon at three. There were also officers of the Society of the Cincinnati meeting in Philadelphia, and there was much dining together and talking and Mason was more hopeful of agreement than he had been before.

He feared that John would not be able to hear the debates, for there was a growing desire that the deliberations of the Convention should be kept secret until the great plan was fully drawn up, and in another letter to George, written a week later, he said:

"It is expected our doors will be shut and communications upon the business of the Convention be forbidden during its sitting. This I think myself a proper precaution to prevent mistakes and misrepresentation until the business shall have been completed, when the whole may have a very different complexion from that in which the several crude and indigested parts might in their first shape appear."

General Washington had been unanimously elected President

of the Convention on the 26th and a committee was appointed
to draw up rules for the convention itself.

Of this committee George Wythe of Virginia was elected
chairman, and Alexander Hamilton of New York and Charles
Pinckney of South Carolina were to serve with him. James
Madison seems to have been acknowledged as the licensed
recorder of the proceedings of the Convention. He kept his
notes in a shorthand of his own and these were not published
until 1840.[178]

It was Governor Randolph of Virginia who spoke first upon
the real business of the Convention. He began with a clear and
courteous statement showing why the Articles of Confederation
had proved inadequate. He then read the fifteen resolutions
of the Virginia Plan and the Convention was under way. When
the Convention ended, the following September, the recorder
was unfortunately absent, but we have Washington's own account
of that last day. He wrote in his journal on September 17, 1787:

"Met in Convention, when the Constitution received the
unanimous vote of eleven states and Colonel Hamilton's from
New York (the only delegate from there in Convention), and
was subscribed to by every member present except Governor
Randolph and Colonel Mason from Virginia, and Mr. Gerry
from Massachusetts.

"The business being thus closed, the members adjourned to the
city tavern, dined together and took a formal leave of each
other . . ."

Between the opening of the convention in May and its closing
in September, the members had met for from five to seven hours
daily except for Sundays, and ten days' adjournment to give
necessary time to a committee. In addition there had been
frequent informal gatherings in a room set aside for the delegates
at the Indian Queen. Here, there were also dinners, when little
groups met to discuss the business of the moment and there was
much drinking of tea and conversation over the teacups. The
stiff etiquette of Philadelphia society bored Mason, but early in
his stay, he drove out with his son and some other gentlemen to

call upon John Bartram whose eight acre garden is acknowledged to be the first botanic garden in this country.[179] The party left Philadelphia in carriages, drove across the Schuylkill, and Bartram was "embarrassed at seeing so large and gay a company so early in the morning." They surprised Mr. Bartram in his bare feet hoeing the garden.[180]

Mason and his son John must have passed another bit of the America-to-come in Philadelphia's Pennsylvania Hospital, founded in 1751 by Benjamin Franklin. It was the first hospital in the United States. Perhaps there the Colonel might have found healing for that anomalous ailment which he called gout in the stomach.

The 82-year-old Franklin was an important and respected member of the Pennsylvania group of delegates. As a nationally admired character, his word carried great weight and his laboratory and inventions were a source of interest to all. There were plays and concerts also for moments of relaxation, and occasional fishing and hunting expeditions in the country around Philadelphia.

The work of the delegates, however, permitted little time for pleasure. Some of the hotly disputed problems in the writing of the constitution were: whether the government should rest upon the people or upon the states; if upon the states, should their representation rest upon their geographical area, or upon the size of their population? Should a state's voting power rest upon its population's size or upon its wealth? The physical differences of the states presented other questions: the lumbermen, the fur traders, the fishermen, the shipowners and the southern planters must all be considered. Slave labor in the south was a subject which was to prove too complex for solution in the Convention. Almost throughout the Convention the questions were debated of how a chief executive should be chosen; should there be more than one? Hamilton and Gouverneur Morris wished to see the country ruled by an aristocracy, or even by a king, and this suggestion was bitterly opposed by the democratically minded members. How long should a chief executive remain in power, and who should choose his advisors and how should they be chosen? Among these advisors to the chief executive, how should the people of all these different states with their different needs be represented? How could the frontiersmen be sure that their interests would not be neglected? Would the fewer numbers of Southern states see their interests obscured by the demands of North, East and West? . . . The weather was hot and muggy and men's tempers grew short.

At this point, the revered Franklin arose to remind the members that they had been sent there, "to consult, not to contend," and he added, "Declarations of fixed opinion and of determined resolution never to change it, neither enlighten nor convince us."

Now the type of government to be desired was discussed. They were making no progress.

Mason thought Franklin was taking a leaf from Libby's book, who when the outlook was black had suggested that Nancy take the "uplook". The old Dr. Franklin pulled his large and now shapeless body out of his chair and, standing before the Convention, suggested that, since man alone was proving himself insufficient, they open the lecture sessions with prayer. Alexander Hamilton feared that an appeal to "foreign aid" would cause the world to question the unity of the Convention. There was, however, little unity at that time and the other members appear not to have considered God to be foreign. Governor Randolph suggested that after the Fourth of July sermon to the members, the practice be adopted of opening the meetings with prayer, and Hamilton was, no doubt, as glad as the rest to adopt Randolph's suggestion.[181]

Pinckney made the suggestion that the matter of suffrage be referred to a committee of one member from each state and that they consider the matter during Independence Day recess. Sherman, the delegate from Connecticut, who was the son of a shoemaker, voiced everyone's sentiments when he said, "We are now at full stop and no one, I suppose, intended that we should break up without doing something."

The delegates took their Fourth of July recess and, with rest, came a perspective upon the problems before them. There had been a break in the heat, too, and the exhausted patriots separated for a few days and went hunting or fishing. Those unfortunate ones appointed to committees were forced to remain. Washington revisited Valley Forge. No record remains to tell us whether Colonel Mason went fishing with John or whether he remained quietly in his room to rest and write letters.

When the Convention met again on July 5th, he expressed his determination to see the task finished. In his speech that day he said:

". . . I would bury my bones in this city rather than expose my country to the consequences of a dissolution of the Convention without anything being done."[182]

30

Up to this time George Mason had taken part with equanimity in the discussions, and in them he had shown his usual wisdom, that wisdom which in past years had so often found utterance by the lips of others who had stopped at Gunston Hall and then gone on to Richmond, to Alexandria or to Philadelphia, there to express the thoughts of the Sage of Gunston. Since the first deliberations of the Convention, he had more than once influenced the delegates to make decisions which have stood the test of time. His own innate wisdom now rose to his country's need, trained as it was in his youth by John Mercer, developed by the circumstances of his own life as Justice of Fairfax County Court, Vestryman of Truro Parish, master of the many souls upon a great plantation, father of a large family of motherless children and author of the Declaration of Rights and Constitution of Virginia. Now, however, he was to find in the Federal Convention a situation in which he would meet apparent defeat and keen disappointment. Furthermore, his defeat would lead inexorably to that which he so greatly dreaded, "misery of millions yet unborn". Not until long after his death and after the deaths of many descendants of the men who sat with him in that summer of 1787, would Mason's ideal of "no slavery" in this country be realized.

Not only his slaves should be freed, he believed, but all slaves. This task must be accomplished gradually, with the good of the entire country kept constantly in mind. It must not be done suddenly. The negro must be educated and helped to be self-supporting before he was cast upon his own resources and made to fend for himself. Otherwise he would suffer and become a burden on the whole community, which would suffer also. When Thomas Jefferson spoke of George Mason as a man of "the first order of greatness" perhaps he referred to Mason's anxiety to put the well-being of his country above all selfish interests.

Now, in the Convention, the different parts of the country were upon the defensive, each part seeking its own interests. The South wished its exports to go out and its slaves to come in, just as they were then doing, and with no governmental interference. The North wanted protection for its manufacturing, already one of its greatest interests; and its shipowners, free of hampering British navigation laws, foresaw an opulent future and desired every help from the government. A Committee on Detail had been appointed when Pinckney rose for South Carolina and "reminded the Convention that if the Committee should fail to insert some security to the Southern States against an emancipation of slaves and taxes on exports, he should be bound by duty to his state to vote against their report." The North now came forward, equally determined that its interests should not be overlooked.

As Helen Hill tells us in her excellent book, *George Mason, Constitutionalist,* Mason was the leader of a third group "composed of both Northerners and Southerners, who wished to treat slavery as a social institution, rather than as the raw materials of bargaining power."[183]

The reserved and dignified planter, now upon his feet, poured forth an impassioned plea that the slave trade be discontinued. He said:[184]

"This infernal traffic originated in the avarice of British merchants. The British Government constantly checked the attempts of Virginia to put a stop to it. The present question concerns not the importing States alone, but the whole Union.

Maryland and Virginia have already prohibited the importation of slaves expressly. North Carolina has done the same in substance. All this will be in vain, if South Carolina and Georgia be at liberty to import. The Western people are already calling out for slaves for their new lands; and will fill that country with slaves if they can be got through South Carolina and Georgia. Slavery discourages arts and manufacturing. The poor despise labor when performed by slaves. They prevent the emigration of whites who really enrich and strengthen a country. They produce the most pernicious effect on manners. Every master of slaves is born a petty tyrant. They bring the judgment of heaven on a country. As nations cannot be rewarded or punished in the next world, they must be in this. By an inevitable chain of causes and effects, Providence punishes national sins by national calamities. It is lamentable that some of our Eastern brethren have, from a lust of gain, embarked on this nefarious traffic. As to the states having the right to import, this is the case with many other rights, now to be properly given up. It is essential, from every point of view, that the general government should have power to prevent the increase of slavery."

Mason took his seat and Ellsworth of Connecticut was on his feet at once. Apparently he saw in Mason's speech an affront to the Eastern States and not a challenge to each to consider the well-being of all.

"As I have never owned a slave," Ellsworth said, "I cannot judge of the effects of slavery on character. If, however, it is to be considered in a moral light, we ought to go further and free those already in the country. In Virginia and Maryland," he added, "it is cheaper to raise slaves than to import them, but in the sickly rice swamps of South Carolina and Georgia foreign supplies are necessary. To stop the slaves trade would therefore be unjust to the states in the extreme south. Let us not," he ended, "intermeddle. As population increases, poor laborers will be so plenty as to render slaves useless. Slavery, in time, will not be a speck in our country."[185]

Oliver Ellsworth having spoken for Connecticut, handsome Charles Pinckney spoke for South Carolina.

"Slavery," he said, "is justified by the example of all the world." South Carolina and Georgia, he told the Convention, could not do without slaves, and Virginia, he believed, would do well without importing them. Those she already had would rise in value. He then proceeded to prove the value of slavery to the entire country. "The more slaves, the more produce to employ the carrying trade; the more consumption also, and the more of this, the more revenue for the common treasury." To end the slave trade, he said, would be to exclude South Carolina from the United States.[186]

At last Gouverneur Morris suggested that "these things (in which he included taxes on exports and a navigation act) may form a bargain between the Northern and Southern States."

With this so called "bargain," began the change in the Constitution into which Mason had hoped to write all the idealism included in his Virginia Declaration of Rights. Here, practical materialism paved the way to blood and tears, where Mason's higher motives would, in the end, have proved practical.

It was now the end of August and the exact wording of the Constitution called for the Convention's close study.[187] This was Mason's especial gift. Still hopeful of attaining his ideals for the Constitution, no word or phrase escaped his close scrutiny. The idea of a legislature composed of two houses was his preference. The chief executive, he thought, should be elected for seven years, his pardoning power should not include cases of treason, and his power to make appointments should be considered very carefully by the Convention. In all branches of the legislature, Mason was anxious to guard against corruption. The selection of the privy council was discussed and the manner of selecting the chief executive.

Mason moved the substitution of the House for the Senate as the deciding body.[188] He feared a too powerful Senate.

One of his especial concerns was the protection of the interests of the Northwest Territory.

"If the Western States," he said "are to be admitted into the Union as they arise, they must be treated as equals and be subjected to no degrading discriminations."[189]

The Convention provided for the admission of new states to the Union and for the setting aside of a district "not exceeding ten miles square," which was to become the city of Washington, and there were many other carefully thought-through matters. Mason's hopes still dwelt upon ending the importation of slaves and upon the inclusion of a Bill of Rights in the Constitution. He was discontented with the power given Congress to pass navigation acts "which would enable a few rich merchants in Philadelphia, New York and Boston to monopolize the staples of the Southern States and reduce their value, perhaps fifty per-cent." He moved "that no law in the nature of a navigation act be passed before the year 1808, without the consent of two-thirds of each branch of the legislature."[190]

The motion was *not* carried. The importation of slaves was *not* stopped. A Bill of Rights was *not* included.

Mason seconded Edmund Randolph's motion "that amendments to the plan might be offered by the State Conventions, which should be submitted to and finally decided on by another general convention." This motion also was defeated.

As the Constitution now stood, Mason felt that he could neither sign it nor give it his support in the Virginia Assembly.

On the 17th of September, Doctor Franklin opened the final ceremony, saying that he "doubted whether any other Convention we can obtain may be able to make a better Constitution."

With bitter disappointment, Mason watched the signatures affixed while he, Edmund Randolph and Elbridge Gerry, alone, withheld their names.

On the 23rd of the following June, Virginia ratified the Constitution and on the 25th the Committee on amendments reported a Bill of Rights. Mason had served upon this committee and the new bill bore a close resemblance to the Bill of Rights of Virginia, but it had long to wait before its inclusion in the Constitution. It was eventually acted upon by the first Federal Congress.

31

A STORM HAD SWEPT OVER THE Potomac. Now it was finished and George Mason stood before the land front of Gunston Hall savoring the Spring's promise of fulfillment. This he detected in the fragrance exuded by moist earth, in the tender green and feathery white of his blackheart cherry trees, and in the joyous chorus of peepers in the marsh. An old foxhound stood beside him, looking up at his master with the morose adoration peculiar to his breed. In a litter of splendid hunters, all proud descendants of old Rion, Plato had proved a disappointment to the young Mason men. Plato had a fine nose, but he was deaf and therefore useless in the hunting field. He had, however, attached himself to Old Master and the affection had become mutual. Colonel Mason declared Plato was an old man's dog and a philosopher. He had named him Plato and taken him for his own.

"Well, Plato," the Colonel said, "shall we walk down to the white gate?"

Even with a cane, the Colonel still carried himself with an air. His hair required no powder now. It was quite white. His face had grown more aquiline with age, and combined with the sharpness of his eyes, gave him the look of an old eagle. On his journey down the roadway, he stopped from time to time to examine his cherry trees, tapping with his cane at an occasional unsound branch.

Halfway to the white gate his ear caught the sound of hoof-beats. The letter carrier perhaps? When would he have news that the Bill of Rights had been ratified by the States? When would it become a part of the Constitution? His neighbor, George Washington, was now President of the United States and was, at this very moment, in the third week of April, 1789, on his way to New York to take up his new duties.

Mason had ridden to Mount Vernon to bid him Godspeed. They had had a few moments conversation, alone on the piazza, and Washington had looked wistfully at the river which he would leave so soon. They had spoken of the Bill of Rights, and the new first President had said he would request his first Congress to make its inclusion in the Constitution its first concern. He had said:

"I shall ask them to consider how the characteristic rights of free men . . . can be impregnably fortified . . ."[192]

Then, turning to his old friend, Washington had given Mason one of his piercing and kindly looks.

"And for you yourself," he asked, "what service in the power of the people can I bestow on you?"

George Mason's reply had been instantaneous and accompanied by one of his courtly bows:

"Your service, sir," he had said, "as President of the United States."

And now the President was on his way; the ratification of the Bill of Rights would follow. Spring was bursting all around him and if he missed the companionship of John who was in France, and of Thomas[193] who was studying at the Academy in Fredericksburg, his gay and sweet Betsy, who was still un-married and at home, and an increasing number of grand-children, were a continual source of pleasure, pride and enter-tainment. He had now reached the gate and opened it as riders approached down the hawthorn-bordered drive. The trees were bursting into pink bloom and Mason saw that it was Betsy, accom-panied by young William Thornton, who rode toward him. She was in a green riding habit, a small green hat sat jauntily upon her curls, and a feather curled beguilingly down to her shoulder. Her cheeks were as rosy as the cloud of hawthorn blossoms, and Colonel Mason smiled with the look of mingled pride and love peculiar to fathers.

The horses were halted and the young people dismounted, and leading their horses, walked back to the house, one on either side of the Colonel. There was to be a party, it seemed at Rippon Lodge.

"I can't think what I shall wear!" Betsy exclaimed with exaggerated anxiety, adding that there had been a young lady from Charleston at a party at the Fowkes' in Maryland last week, who had worn a dress of striped silk lately brought from Paris. Betsy was not demanding but a bit wistful, and the Colonel decided at once that John should buy some silk for her in Paris. He must write John a long letter as soon as possible.

The letter he wrote is still in existence.[194] It was full of good advise, of news from home and of the political scene, and he tells his son that he has just sent him "by Capt. Bond, a barrel containing eight hams. I wish they may arrive in good order, as I think they were exceedingly good hams when they were packed up.[195] I should be glad to know whether the barrel of hominy and smoked beef by Capt. Rose got to hand in good order. Your brothers sent you by Capt. Rose two female and one male opossum."

John, at Bordeaux, was in business with a Mr. Fenwick and disappointed not to have received more tobacco than had arrived. His father wrote:

"You are under obligations to Mr. Daniel Brent of "Richlands" and his brother, Mr. Richard Brent, for their utmost endeavors to promote your interest here, and I believe to very good effect. Your Stafford friends have not shipped you so generally as I expected. One reason for that is that a great part of their tobacco upon low grounds was destroyed by the excessive rains last summer, and another that I believe many of them are indebted to the Scotch stores and there is hardly a Scotch merchant in this part of the country who does not wish your house at the devil."

Perhaps Colonel Mason remembered, as he wrote this, that his father had once, for his assistance to Scottish merchants, been made a free man of the City of Glasgow.

Mason hoped that his son and Mr. Fenwick had gone to housekeeping, for as he wrote:

"There are of course many captains of ships and others to whom it will be necessary for you to show civilities."

He could not feel it would be any great addition to their expense and added that it would give some respectability to their business house.

"I still continue of the opinion," he wrote, "that it will be very imprudent in you to come to America this year but that it will be very proper the year after."

This was because of the activity of pirates operating from the African Coast on the Mediterranean.

He referred to an important affair with a Mr. Whitesides in which he felt John had been lax in not being entirely aware of what was going on. He wrote:

". . . You should spare no pains or application to make yourself well acquainted with business, so as to be able to take a proper share in the management, as well as to enable you to conduct the business of a separate house yourself whenever it becomes necessary which probably may be soon . . . This affair," he said, "gives me much uneasiness, for though I have always heard a very good character of Mr. Fenwick and that he is a diligent, attentive, discreet young man, yet this transaction shows a kind of softness and milkiness of temper liable to imposition which both you and he ought to guard against."

There is a request for silk for Betsy and a request that he select it himself, and the letter ends with the charming news that they had a mockingbird for him. It was a disappointment, however, for it proved to be a female and would therefore not sing, and he would not send it to France, "to disgrace its native country."

"I would turn it out of its cage", he said, "but I am afraid its liberty, after much long confinement, would only make the poor thing a prey to the first hawk that came its way."

They would raise some young ones in the coming summer and also a buck and doe fawn for the boy, now so far away, who had loved the wild creatures on the plantation at home.

The following year the Richmond paper published the news that "the Hon. George Mason, Esq. is appointed as Senator of the United States,"[196] but Colonel Mason's public service was over. He wrote John about it, putting it at the very end of a letter and saying tersely, that he had refused to serve.

In the same letter he commented on the French Revolution, now in full swing. He said:[197]

"I heartily wish the French nation success in establishing their new government upon the principles of liberty and the sacred rights of human nature, but I dread the consequences of their affairs remaining so long in an unsettled state . . . besides the risk of the most respectable part of the people (which is always found in the middle walks of life) being disgusted and worn down with so long a scene of doubt and uncertainty, not to say anarchy."

He had been ill for three months with gout and after twenty years service, had resigned as justice of Fairfax County. Sarah was alarmed at the depression of spirit that accompanied his illness. He longed for the understanding of the men with whom he had worked most closely for his country's benefit, and she was grateful for the reassurance he received in a letter from Mr. Jefferson,[198] who had returned from Paris in 1789 to take his place in Washington's Cabinet. He and George Mason had been carrying on a lively correspondence; Jefferson glad to avail himself of Mason's judgments, and Mason eager to keep in touch with the march of events. Mason had feared that Washington's regard for him might have altered.[199] Now it appeared to him that Madison also was disappointed in the stand he had taken. Disillusionment was worse than illness, and it seemed at times that only his conscience supported him. But Jefferson wrote[200] of their mutual friend Madison: ". . . I have always heard him say that though you and he appeared to differ in your systems, yet you were, in truth, nearer together than most persons who were classed under the same appellation. You may quiet yourself in the assurance of possessing his complete esteem."

He added, "Certainly, whenever I pass your road, I shall do myself the pleasure of turning in to it."

It was a gloomy day in February, 1791 when the letter came, and Sarah had been busy with a sick negress in the quarters near the house. Coming back through the herb garden, its dejected winter look seemed to her to accord well with her own soul. George had seemed so depressed that morning. She must find some cheerful happening, she thought, for this grey day. Perhaps Elizabeth would bring the children over from Lexington . . .

As she came down the long passage into the hall, she saw her husband walking toward the door. He was dressed, as he always was, in black. They had been married ten years but he still wore mourning for the beloved Ann. If Sarah had ever held any illusions about taking her place they would certainly have been gone by now. Sometimes she felt he considered her much as he did the female mockingbird, which could not sing but must not be released for fear a hawk would kill it. George had saved her from a human hawk, and like the little bird, she had no gift with which to charm him.

"Come, Sarah," she said to herself, "enough of this. What should an old woman like me do with charm? I am as necessary to him as air to breathe, and he is to me, life itself."

She saw him take a letter from the German coachman who had replaced Peter.

"I hope it is something happy-" she thought.

A few minutes later he came to find her, the letter in his hand. She went with him into his little sitting room and shared the pleasure, interest and comfort which Jefferson's words gave him. Sarah looked at him lovingly as he read the letter through. It seemed to her that his white hair added to his distinction, and his beautifully shaped hands never failed to delight her with their look of ability and sensitive kindliness. They could still shoot with amazing accuracy as well as write a Bill of Rights. They could bandage a negro's cuts and hold a captive nightingale unfrightened. She noticed another letter on the candlestand beside him and was delighted to hear that it had come from George Rogers Clark.

After the war, they learned, Clark had lost his commission and that having been in the militia, he was now entitled to no pay from the regular army. He had been reduced to poverty. He was still under forty, but his country had forgotten him, although he had spent his private fortune in feeding and fitting out his men.

"His glory will come later," Sarah said. "Perhaps there was something in the story Mrs. Cockburn told Nancy and Nancy repeated to me."

"What was that?" Mason was all interest.

"She said," Sarah explained, "that there was a tradition in his family that the dark-haired Clarks would meet with worldly success but that the red-haired ones would win the world, only to give it away."

"I'm afraid that is true in this case," the Colonel admitted, "but I cannot feel that when our history is written the people of the land he has opened will forget a young man who thought, not of himself, but of his country."

The Colonel had saved the best letter till last. He drew it from his pocket now as a surprise. John had set a definite date for his return. It was still six months away but it was something to be anticipated with happiness. Mr. Fenwick would remain in Bordeaux where Colonel Mason's influence had procured him the post of Consul, but John would return and build up the business on this side of the water.

He would take a tour, Mason decided, through the Eastern States and another in the South. Which would it be better to do first? What did Sarah think? He was animated and full of interest and they both were surprised when Sampson announced dinner. As he rose, the Colonel drew Sarah's arm through his, patting her hand gently as he did so.

"Sarah, my dear," he said "You are a sweet woman. You

carry comfort and sunlight with you. Where should I be without your love?"

Sarah, her eyes swimming, raised them nevertheless to his and said, "Not so lost as I should be without yours, I think!"

32

CHRISTMAS, 1791 brought all the children home. John and Tom came down from Alexandria together. Tom was living in Alexandria, and John was now on Analostion Island, between Georgetown and the site of the future city of Washington, where Mr. L'Enfant was already at work planning the new capital.

They found Gunston Hall full of children and grandchildren, fires on all the once-cold hearths, and holly and mistletoe in a great bunch tied to the pineapple of welcome in the hall arch. Sally's oldest child had blossomed into a reigning belle in her own right, carrying on the tradition of her mother and grandmother, and she had decorated the lapel of her grandfather's black silk coat with a bunch of bright red holly berries. The dining table was so long that the smallest children were seated at a smaller table near the window and the whistling boys were helping again in the dining room, travelling their syncopated way from kitchen to dining table under Sampson's now nearsighted direction. More than one turkey leg vanished unnoticed on its journey from the kitchen that day.

When it was over, the various family coaches bore away the parents and children. They left the Master of Gunston Hall happy and tired with a deep sense of gratitude for the blessings of his life.

There was still another fulfillment for George Mason before the year ended. The looked-for letter came at last. The Bill of

Christmas at Gunston Hall

Rights had been pushed through its slow stages of ratification by the states, and, on December 15th, 1791, when the 11th state gave its approval, the first ten amendments became a part of the Constitution of the the United States.[201]

Thomas Jefferson continued to stop at Gunston Hall whenever it was possible for him to do so, and George Mason looked forward with especial pleasure and interest to his visits.

Kate Mason Rowland says of these two men:[202]

"Thomas Jefferson, so soon to become the leader of a triumphant Republican (or Democratic) party, which was to carry out in government, as far as possible, the states rights views of George Mason, turned with the affection and reverence of a disciple to the retired sage of Gunston Hall."

Jefferson has left in the *Anas* his own account of George Mason's views on September 30, 1792. Mason had been ill, but he was about again, and the two friends discussed the Federal Convention and its work. Jefferson tells us that "the Constitution as agreed to till a fortnight before the Convention rose, was such a one as he [Mason] would have set his hand and heart to."

It would have contained these provisions, he quotes:

"1. The President was to be elected for seven years, then ineligible for seven years more."

"2. Rotation in the Senate."

"3. A vote of two-thirds on particular subjects, and expressly on that of navigation".

"The three New England states were constantly with us in all questions, Rhode Island not there and New York seldom; so that it was these three states, with the five Southern States, against Pennsylvania, New Jersey and Delaware. With respect to the importation of slaves, it was left to Congress. This disturbed the two southernmost states, who knew that Congress would immediately suppress the importation of slaves. Those two states, therefore, struck up a bargain with the three New England States, that if they would join to admit slaves for some years, the two southernmost states would join in changing the clause which required two-thirds of the legislature in any vote.

It was done. The articles were changed accordingly and from that moment the two southernmost states and the three northern ones joined Pennsylvania, Jersey and Delaware and made the majority of eight to three against us, instead of eight to three for us, as it had been through the whole Convention."

The two friends were seated on the octagonal porch upon the river front of Gunston Hall. As Mason talked, Jefferson noted down his words with paper and a quill pen James had brought him for the purpose. There were some anecdotes of the Convention and Jefferson wrote those down too. Both men were aware of children's voices in the garden beyond the foot of the steps. Two little granddaughters were playing house under the now tall box bushes that bordered the vista straight from the door of the house to the end of the terrace. Beyond, the Potomac glistened silver in the September haze. Now and then, a little pink or blue frock fluttered into sight and was lost again in that primeval forest of box which was childhood's kingdom. The drone of bees added its music to the children's soft voices and a little negro voice, also from under the box, added its own peculiar sweetness. What anguish those children might have been spared had the Convention heeded more carefully the voice of the Master of Gunston!

Jefferson looked at his watch and rose. The ride to Mount Vernon lay ahead of him and he feared he had tired his host. Sarah, just within, in the hall, heard the men stirring and appeared with a quick anxious glance at her husband. From the direction of the kitchen, Mammy was calling, and the children scampered obediently out from under the box. Mr. Jefferson made his courtly bow.

"Good night, Madam," he said, "and good night, Sir, to the author of Virginia's Declaration of Rights and Constitution, inspiration of the first part of the Declaration of Independence (and who should know this better than I?) and now of the Bill of Rights of the United States, for we all know whence it came! Take care of him," he added to Sarah with a smile, "and I will return on my way home."

He had gone. Sarah took his place and for a few moments both remained silent. Mason, touched by Jefferson's tribute, did not dare at first, to speak. When he did, his voce trembled.

"My work is done, Sarah," he said, "but it is not finished. States' rights and slavery, they will have to be settled. I had hoped to see it completed."

Sarah took his hand and her touch was warm and strong. "My dear, my dear," she said, "how often have you told me to remember that Rome was not built in a day! You have planted a great Nation. Its seed is the belief in the God-given, natural rights of man. It will face storms and bitter winds. It will endure floods and parching heat. But it will endure. It is a small, new thing now, but we have had a glimpse, just a glimpse, my dear, of the coming glory."

George Mason tightened his hold upon her hand.

"Thank you, Sarah," he said. "Thank you. I will be content with my glimpse of glory."

He leaned back, still holding her hand. The sun was going down and its golden light flooded garden, countryside and river. From the quarters on the left floated the mellow, rich notes of a negro "hymn tune". The words were lost but the music carried its message of undying faith.

It was almost time for George Mason to rest.

Epilogue

Today, an old house sits dreaming. Like the very old who are also very great, it has left all bitterness behind. There is a sweetness in its age like the sweetness of its youth. Hungry it has been for the activity of its early days, for the heaped work-basket by the chair beside the fire, for the disordered sheets of music on the spinet, for the mud of the Master's riding boots on the step, and the doll forgotten in the hall.

Truly the house has its memories of laughter and tears, but like old Sherry this is all refined by time to a dry and golden sweetness, and from the past a hope is distilled which is today's *Glimpse of Glory!*

Footnotes

[1]Thomas Tilleston Waterman in *Mansions of Virginia.*

[2]Pronounced "Brood."

[3]Article by Miss Mary Wakefield of Breewood—*Staffordshire Life,* March, 1952.

[4]A similar locket was found recently by Lord Monson and is now in the Lord Monson collection in England.

[5]Kate Mason Rowland.

[6]*Ibid.*

[7]*Ibid.*

[8]*Ibid.*

[9]*Ibid.*

[10]*Ibid.*—In old surveys, Necks are often called Islands.

[11]*Ibid.*

[12]1953.

[13]Kate Mason Rowland—Vol. I, p. 29.

[14]*Ibid.*

[15]Prince William County Deed Book A, pages 280-281 and 352-353, deeds dated 1731 and 1732 from George Mason, late of the County of Stafford, but now of Charles County, Md., Gent. (In the Parish of Durham.)

[16]Blue was the color predominant in the Mason's coat-of-arms.

[17]Kate Mason Rowland.

[18]Mrs. Mason's much loved Nan Old Gate was left in her will to George Mason with the request that no more work be required of her.

[19]This list is taken from Fithian's list of the books of Robert Carter, books now preserved in the book cupboard at Kenmore in Fredericksburg.

[20]*The Brent Family*—William Chilton.

[21]Mattawoman, the old Eilbeck plantation where Colonel and Mrs. William Eilbeck are buried, lies near "Araby," the house where Ann Eilbeck lived as a girl. "Araby" is now the property of Admiral and Mrs. Jack Fletcher and stands on the road from LaPlata to Indian Head in Maryland.

[22]General Smallwood, their son, later commanded the Maryland troops in the battle of Long Island. There, on Brooklyn Heights, their bravery saved Washington and the American cause.

[23]Great Arab progenitor of Virginia's finest horses in Colonial times.

[24]Now destroyed, though some of its bricks are believed used in its successor. This Maryland Gunston Hall is still occupied by descendants of Gerrard Fowke. The English Gunston Hall is gone—traces of its foundations remain in the orchard. A newer house bears the name.

[25]*Martha's Husband* by Blair Niles—p. 5.

[26]"Roses and lilies, almost without a metaphor," he said of her in the notice he wrote of her death.

[27]*Tidewater Maryland,* Wilstach, pp. 95 and 298.

[28]*Ibid.*

[29]*Virginia's Mother Church* by Brydon, p. 133.

[30]Moncure was rector of Overwharton Parish but the church there was not built till a year later. Brydon.

[31]*Virginia's Eastern Shore* by Ralph Whitelaw, Va. Hist. Soc.

[32]Letters of *Mollie Tilghman in Tidewater Maryland* by Paul Wilstach.

[33]Mary Hodge who became Mrs. West, married at Hope Lodge, White Marsh, Pa. From *History of American Costume* by Elizabeth McClellan.

[34]Falbalas or furbelows were rows of pleating or puffs fashionable in the time of William and Mary.

[35]*George Mason: Constitutionalist* by Helen Hill, Harvard University Press.

[36]Mary Selden died while still a young woman.

[37]George Mason's own words, quoted in *The Story of the Constitution of the United States* by Charles W. Ervin and Jo Davidson, page 33.

[38]George Mason's own words.

[39]*Virginia, A Guide to the Old Dominion* says built about 1725.

[40]*Tidewater Maryland* by Paul Wilstach, page 95.

[41]These patches of Mayapples are said to be Indian plantings. *History of Horticulture in America* by Hedrick, Pub. Oxford Press.

[42]His portrait by Charles Wilson Peale is in Yale University Art Gallery.

[43]Inventory of his goods and chattels quoted in *Md. Hist. Mag.* Sept. 1946, Article by Rosamond Randall Beirne.

[44]It is not certain that James Buckland, bookseller, was Wm. Buckland's uncle.

[45]Thomas Tilleston Waterman in *Mansions of Virginia*, University of North Carolina Press, pp. 222-231.

[46]Annotated indenture papers found in the Maryland Archives.

[47]Mary Moore is mentioned by Rosamond Randall Beirne as Buckland's wife. See article *Md. Hist. Mag.*, Sept. 1946.

[48]George Mason, in a letter addressed to the Public Ledger in London and to the Committee for Merchants in London, January 6, 1766.

[49]*Daily National Intelligencer*—Washington, Nov. 16, 1840.

[50]Some writers say that Ann Eilbeck was George Washington's "Lowland Maid," others that it was Mrs. Lee, the mother of Richard Henry Lee; still others that it was neither.

[51]The old name for this road was given by Mrs. Calvin Bruce Matthews, a descendant of George Mason.

[52]From his will.

[53]Washington's Diary.

[53a]See *Virginia's Eastern Shore,* by Ralph Whitelaw, p. 30.

[54]Letter in the Library of Congress, Washington, D. C.

[55]*Virginia's Eastern Shore*—Whitelaw, p. 30.

[56]Pronounced "Coburn."

[57]Pronounced "with."

[58]Now the home of Mr. and Mrs. Donald W. Vought and known as Windsor Shades.

[59]*The Tidewater Review,* April 24, 1952.

[60]Clark's one existing letter to Mason.

[61]That December's family records show the birth and death of twin boys. Their deaths were believed caused by Mrs. Mason's ill health at the time.

[62]Overseers mentioned by Kate Mason Rowland—Vol. II, p. 348.

[63]Later he became physician to George Washington, also.

[64]*Review of Nursing*—Hansen.

[65]Kate Mason Rowland, Vol. I, p. 163.

[66]Archibald Rutledge in *It Will Be Daybreak Soon.*

[67]*Virginia Cavalcade* Summer number 1951.

[68]*Ibid.*

[69]Kate Mason Rowland, Vol. I, p. 297 "My eldest daughter . . . manages my little domestic matters with a degree of prudence far above her years."

[70]From *Washington and Mount Vernon,* Lossing, pp. 23 and 24.

[71]*Williamsburg in Virginia* by Rutherford Goodwin.

[71a]Bellamy, *The Private Life of George Washington,* N. Y. 1951, p. 164 says: "To refuse to acknowledge that he (Mason) must have built a slow fire under Washington, is to be unrealistic."

[72]*The Heir of Douglas* by Lillian Delatorre, Pub. Knoff.

[73]Years later, George Graham married the widow of George Mason V.

[74]Copy of Fairfax Resolves in appendix.

[75]The first schooner is said to have been built in Gloucester, Mass. in 1713.

[76]From an address by Edward Boykin, Director, National Capitol Sesquicentennial Commission at Mt. Vernon, May 19, 1949.

[77]*Eleanor Calvert and Her Circle* by Alice Coyle Torbert.

[78]*George Mason: Constitutionalist* by Helen Hill.

[79]George Washington's Diary.

[80]Letter from Mason to his cousin, George Mercer, in London.

[81]Kate Mason Rowland—Vol. I, p. 182.

[82]Kate Mason Rowland—Vol. I, p. 183.

[83]"This plan is considered the forerunner of Mason's greatest pronouncements on political liberty."—Edward Boykin.

[84]Kate Mason Rowland.

[85]*Ibid.*

[86]*The Conquest* by Eva Emery Dye—Pub. Grosse & Dunlap, N. Y. 1902.

[87]Statement of the Maryland Provincial Committee as quoted by Helen Hill in *George Mason: Constitutionalist.*

[88]*Ibid.*

[89]Bermudians today show where it was kept.

[90]*George Mason: Constitutionalist*—Helen Hill.

[91]*George Mason: Constitutionalist*—Helen Hill.

[92]*Ibid.*

[93]Description given by the Mount Vernon Ladies Ass'n.—Robert B. Fisher, Horticulturist.

[94]*George Mason: Constitutionalist*—Helen Hill.

[95]Kate Mason Rowland, Vol. I, p. 195.

[96]*Ibid.*

[97]*George Mason: Constitutionalist*—Helen Hill. Note 35.

[98]Kate Mason Rowland, Vol. I, p. 350.

[99]Recalled by Mason descendants today.

[100]Kate Mason Rowland, Vol. I, p. 195.

[101]When Sarah Brent was brought by her parents from Bermuda, Little Codger was brought to Virginia too. From *Gen. Geo. Mason Graham of Tyrone Plantation* by G. M. G. Stafford.

[102]*Potomac Landings*—Paul Wilstach.

[103]*George Mason* by Kate Mason Rowland, Vol. I, p. 213.

[104]*Ibid.*

[105]*Mary and Martha Washington* by J. B. Lossing, p. 137. Extract from an old newspaper.

[106]The *Fowey,* the *Ruebuck,* the *Mercury,* the *Otter.*

[107]Letter from George Mason to George Washington. October 14, 1775.

[108]Kate Mason Rowland.

[109]*Potomac River Landings*—Wilstach.

[110]*Fythian's Diary.*

[111]*Tidewater Maryland*—Wilstach.

[112]*Fythian's Diary* says the dining room was much used in this way.

[113]Kate Mason Rowland, Vol. I, p. 214.

[114]*Pictorial History of the American Revolution.* Pub. 1845 by Robert Sears.

[115]Kate Mason Rowland, Vol. I, p. 223.

[116]Ms. *History of Virginia.* Quoted by Kate Mason Rowland.

[117]Letter from Thomas Ludwell Lee to his brother Richard Henry Lee, Kate Mason Rowland.

[118]Mason's letter of May 18th to Richard Henry Lee.

[119]John Augustine Washington's letter to Richard Henry Lee.

[120]Ms. letter, Kate Mason Rowland, Vol. I, pp. 226-27.

[121]Kate Mason Rowland, Vol. I, p. 229.

[122]Letter from George Mason to his cousin George Mercer in England, 2nd October, 1778, enclosing a copy of the Bill of Rights and declaring himself to be the author.

[123]Kate Mason Rowland, Vol. I, pp. 252 and 253. Quoting Jefferson's works, Vol. VII, p. 405.

[124]Cromwell's Government gave a Constitution, but with less freedom.

[125]In this country, English Common Law remains unchanged to this day though many statutes have been added.

[126]R. Carter Pittman, an authority on Mason manuscripts.

[127]*Virginia's Mother Church*, Brydon.

[128]Letter dated June 23, 1776.

[129]One of the negroes who came to Nancy under her father's will, Mss. Library of Congress.

[130]Information on the British fleets is from *The Battle of Long Island* by Thomas W. Field, Brooklyn 1869. Entered According to Act of Congress for the L. I. Hist. Soc.

[131]*Ibid.*

[132]*Ibid.*

[133]*Battle of Long Island,* Field. Quoting American Archives, Vol I, 5th Series, folio 1232, writer unknown.

[134]A copy of this prescription is in the N. Y. Public Library Mss. Room.

[135]Retired Dec. 1, 1777. Heitman's *Officers of the Continental Army 1775-1783.*

[136]*Old Virginia Days & Ways* by Sally McCarty Pleasants.

[137]*Love Stories of Famous Virginians,* Sally Nelson Robins.

[138]*The McCartys in Early American History* by O'Brian, Dodd Mead & Co.

[139]Kate Mason Rowland.

[140]Kate Mason Rowland, Vol. I, p. 269.

[141]*Ibid.*

[142]Kate Mason Rowland, Vol. I, p. 276.

[143]*The Conquest,* Eva Emery Dye, A. C. McClurg & Co., 1902.

[144]Kate Mason Rowland, Vol. I, p. 290, quoting Butler's *History of Kentucky,* p. 47 and footnote.

[145]Letter from George Mason, Kate Mason Rowland, Vol. I, p. 295.

[146]Little Codger lived to be over 100 years old and had many descendants. From *General George Mason Graham of Tyrone Plantation* by G. M. G. Stafford.

[147]Mss. Library of Congress and Kate Mason Rowland. The end of the letter is missing.

[148]Kate Mason Rowland.

[149]A tradition in the Mason family—told by Mrs. Calvin Bruce Matthews.

[150]Kate Mason Rowland, Vol. II, p. 2.

[151]Kate Mason Rowland, Vol. II, p. 19, says: "It is very likely that Lafayette was invited to Gunston at this time . . ."

[152]In Colonel Mason's possession at that time was a revolver which had belonged to Captain John Smith. Kate Mason Rowland.

[153]Kate Mason Rowland.

[154]Kate Mason Rowland, Vol. II, pp. 10 and 11.

[155]The Chapman place is called Vue de L'Eau. Kate Mason Rowland.

[156]Of course, this is purely an imaginary happening, as the man, Fanshaw, is a fictitious character.

[157]*Va. Hist. Reg.,* Vol. II, p. 32. Kate Mason Rowland, Vol. II. p. 17. "It seems not unlikely that this interesting and patriotic letter may have had some influence with the French Court and hastened the arrival of the French fleet." She adds that James M. Mason wrote the endorsement on the copy and showed that the original had, by Dr. Franklin, been put into the hands of the Count de Vergennes.

[158]Blair Niles in *Martha's Husband,* p. 191.

[159]Kate Mason Rowland says *"probably* he was there."

[160]Kate Mason Rowland. Vol. II, p. 19.

[161]Nearby Rippon Lodge—still, in 1953, a beautiful place.

[162]Col. Cooke was the son of Sir John Cooke and grandson of Raleigh Travers of Stafford County. Mary Mason married his son John.

[163]Kate Mason Rowland. John Mason later wrote that this was the case with his father.

[164]*The Federalist*—the first number.

[165]Kate Mason Rowland, Vol. II, p. 71.

[166]Kate Mason Rowland, Vol. II, p. 90.

[167]Here the word vulgar seems to be used in its old sense; meaning "of the people—a folk saying."

[168]Kate Mason Rowland, Vol. II, p. 92.

[169]It is in Mason's handwriting. Mr. R. Carter Pittman, authority on Mason manuscripts.

[170]Kate Mason Rowland.

[171]Quoted from a letter to his son, George, June 1, 1787.

[172]Kate Mason Rowland, Vol. II, p. 122. Quoting Madison's report of a speech in the Convention by George Mason.

[173]*The Great Rehearsal,* Carl Van Doren, p. 162.

[174]*Ibid.,* p. 226.

[175]It is a tradition in the Mason family that Washington was, at eighteen, in love with Ann Eilbeck.

[176]*The Great Rehearsal* by Carl Van Doren.

[177]Kate Mason Rowland, Vol. II, pp. 100, 101, 102.

[178]*The Great Rehearsal,* Carl Van Doren, p. 30. *Ibid.,* pp. 31 and 175. Kate Mason Rowland Vol. II, p. 180.

[179]Newsletter by Federated Garden Clubs of New York State Inc. 11&12/1950. Article entitled Our Horticultural Heritage, p. 17, by Mary N. Dixon.

[180]*The Great Rehearsal,* Carl Van Doren, p. 131.

[181]Alice Curtis Desmond—On his death bed Hamilton in mortal agony, recommended to his weeping wife that she remember her religion.

[182]Reported by Madison and quoted by Kate Mason Rowland, Vol. II, p. 133.

[183]*George Mason: Constitutionalist,* Helen Hill.

[184]Kate Mason Rowland, Vol. II, pp. 160, 161, quoting *Madison Papers.*

[185]*The Great Rehearsal* by Carl Van Doren, p. 153.

[186]*The Great Rehearsal,* Carl Van Doren, pp. 153-154.

[187]Kate Mason Rowland, Vol. II, p. 162.

[188]*George Mason: Constitutionalist,* Helen Hill, p. 207.

[189]*George Mason: Constitutionalist,* Helen Hill quoting Madison.

[190]Kate Mason Rowland quoting *Madison Papers,* Vol. III, p. 1308.

[191]*The Rights of Man,* Kurt H. Volk, Inc.

[192]From Washington's Inaugural Address.

[193]Kate Mason Rowland, Vol. II, p. 307.

[194]*Ibid.,* pp. 315-318.

[195]In a subsequent, unpublished letter now at Gunston Hall, Mason spoke again of the hams which had not arrived.

[196]Kate Mason Rowland, Vol. II, p. 325.

[197]*Ibid.,* Vol. II, pp. 326 and 327, date May, 1790.

[198]*Ibid.,* Vol. II, pp. 332 and 333.

[199]*Ibid.,* letter to his son John.

[200]*Ibid.,* letter from Jefferson, Feb. 4th, 1791.

[201]*Life* Magazine—article entitled "Memorable Victories on the Fight for Justice" by Judge Jerome Frank.

[202]Kate Mason Rowland, Vol. II, pp. 362-363.

Acknowledgments

The author makes grateful acknowledgment to the members of The National Society of Colonial Dames of America, of which she is proud to be a member, for their help in research and for their continued encouragement in her quest for information. To them and to the Board of Regents of Gunston Hall is owed the greatest part of the information found in this narrative. The Virginia Historical Society has made priceless manuscripts available and the Maryland Historical Society has been equally helpful. Thanks are due also to the staffs of the Manuscript Room in the Library of Congress and of the Genealogy and Reading Room of the New York Public Library, of the Frick Art Reference Library and of the Burton Historical Collection in the Detroit Public Library. Mr. Edward Morrison of the Manuscript Room of the New York Public Library has been most helpful, as have Mrs. Guy Atkinson, Librarian, and Mrs. Ruth D. Wells, Executive Secretary of the National Society of Colonial Dames in the State of New York, Brigadier General Latane Montague, formerly Director, Mr. Frederick J. Griffiths, Director, and Mr. John P. Cowan of the Fairfax and Falls Church *Sun-Echo*. The writer is especially grateful for books loaned and for time and trouble cheerfully contributed by

Mrs. Lynch Luquer of Washington, D. C.

Mr. R. Carter Pittman of Dalton, Georgia

Mrs. Herbert Claiborne of Richmond, Va., former First Regent of Gunston Hall

Miss Monimia Fairfax MacRae of Asheville, N. C.

Mrs. Chester Woodward of Topeka, Kansas, lately Chairman of Research Committee

Mrs. William Duke of Richmond, Va.

Mrs. Ethelbert Ide Low, former President National Society of Colonial Dames of America and former New York Regent of Gunston Hall

Mrs. William Beverley Mason of Washington, D. C., for the
use of her portraits of George and Ann Mason as illustra-
tions

Mrs. Courtenay Wells Weems, President, National Society of
Colonial Dames in the State of New York

Mrs. Ernest Vietor of New York

Mrs. John Holme Ballantine, 2nd Vice President of the National Society of Colonial Dames of America
and last but far from least

Mrs. Lammot duPont Copeland of Delaware, First Regent of
Gunston Hall

It is the writer's great pleasure to number among her acquaintance some of the descendants of Colonel George Mason who
have been most helpful. She wishes to express her warm thanks
for their interest, for anecdotes recounted from the past and for
their heartening encouragement during the writing of this story,
to

Mrs. Harold D. Crawford of Parkersburg, Regent for West
Virginia

Mrs. Henry B. Thomas of Baltimore, Md., Regent at Large

Mrs. Calvin Bruce Matthews of Washington, D. C.

Mrs. Hoxie Moffett of Washington, D. C.

Mrs. Gilmer Easley of Washington, D. C.

Dr. Davenport West of New York, N. Y.

Bibliography

Critical Period of American History, John Fisk.
Social Life of Virginia in the 17th Century, Philip Alexander Bruce.
George Washington, Douglas Southall Freeman.
George Washington, Rupert Hughes.
Social History of England, G. M. Trevelyan—O.M.
The Young Jefferson, Claud G. Bowers.
Martha Washington, Alice Curtis Desmond.
The Brent Family, William Chilton.
The Descendants of Colonel Giles Brent, Chester Horton Brent.
Tidewater Maryland, Paul Wilstach.
Potomac Landings, Paul Wilstach.
Maryland, American Guide Series.
Maryland Gardens and Houses, compiled by Elizabeth Fisk Clapp,
  Charlton Merrick Gillett, Romaine McI. Randall.
Mansions of Virginia, Thomas Tilleston Waterman.
Philip Vickers Fithian, Edited by H. T. Farish, Colonial Williams-
  burg, Inc.
Robert Carter of Nomini Hall, Morton, Colonial Williamsburg, Inc.
Homes and Gardens in Old Virginia, The Garden Club of Virginia.
Kenmore of the Lewises, Jane Tayler Duke.
Interiors of Virginia Houses of Colonial Times, Edith Tunis Sale.
It Will Be Daybreak Soon, Archibald Rutledge.
George Mason, Life, Correspondence and Speeches, Kate Mason
  Rowland.
History of the American People, Woodrow Wilson.
George Mason, Constitutionalist, Helen Hill.
Review of Nursing, Hansen (1952).
Virginia's Eastern Shore, by Ralph Whitelaw, published by Virginia
  Historical Society.
The Great Rehearsal, Carl Van Doren.
Bulwark of the Republic, Burton J. Hendrick.
Virginia's Mother Church, George Maclaren Brydon, D. D.
Encyclopedia of World History, Houghton Mifflin.
Pictorial History of the American Revolution (1845), Robert Sears.
Eleanor Calvert and Her Circle, Alice Coyle Torbert.
The English Speaking Peoples, Edgar W. McInnis, J. H. S. Reid.
The Southern Colonies in the 17th Century, Wesley Frank Craven.

Martha's Husband, Blair Niles.
Williamsburg in Virginia, Colonial Williamsburg, Inc.
Washington and Mount Vernon, Benson J. Lossing.
Battle of Long Island, Thomas W. Field (Brooklyn 1869).
The Conquest, Eva Emery Dye.
The Rights of Man, Copyright 1950, Kurt H. Volk, Inc.
A History of Maryland, James McSherry (1852).
History of American Costume, Elizabeth McClellan.
Two Centuries of Costume in America, Alice Morse Earle.
Brides and Bridals, J. Cordy Jefferson.
The Piano, Its History, Makers, Players and Music, Albert E. Weir, 1941.
Love Stories of Famous Virginians, Sally Nelson Robins, National Historian Colonial Dames of America.
Old Virginia Days and Ways, Sally McCarty Pleasants.
Washington's Diary.

MAGAZINES AND PAMPHLETS:

Bulletin of The Garden Club of America, *Gunston Hall,* Miss Monimia Fairfax MacRae.
The Private Life of George Washington, Bellamy.
History of Horticulture in America, Hedrick, Oxford Press.
General George Mason Graham of Tyrone Plantation, by George Mason Graham Stafford.
The Heir of Douglas, Lillian Delatorre, published by Knopf.
The Story of the Constitution of the United States, Reported by Charles W. Ervin.
George Mason, An address by Edward Boykin, Director National Capital Sesquicentennial Commission, at Mount Vernon May 19, 1949.
Virginia Cavalcade—Winter 1952, *"A Few Men Well Conducted,"* Exploits of George Rogers Clark, William H. Gaines, Jr.
The Newsletter, Federated Garden Clubs of New York State, Inc., *Our Horticultural Heritage,* Mary Newbury Dixon.
Virginia Cavalcade—Summer, 1951, *George Mason, Spokesman for Human Rights,* Elizabeth Dabney Coleman.
Virginia Cavalcade—Summer 1951, Georgian Gem, *George Mason's Gunston Hall,* Hilda Noel Schroetter.
Virginia Cavalcade—Summer 1951, *The Virginia Declaration of Rights,* William M. E. Rachal.

Lecture, *George Mason of Gunston Hall,* given to National Society of Colonial Dames, Virginia Hunt.

Life Magazine, *Memorable Victories on the Fight for Justice,* Judge Jerome Frank.

Daughters of the American Revolution Magazine, June 1952, *George Mason, Champion of Individual Rights,* Florence S. Berryman.

Maryland Historical Magazine, March 1921, *Colonel Gerard Fowke,* by Gerard Fowke, St. Louis, Mo.—also—September, 1946, *William Buckland,* by R. R. Beirne.

George Mason, His Place in History, an address, Lily Little Ryals, The Macon Town Committee, Georgia Society, Colonial Dames of America.

George Mason, Author of The Virginia Bill of Rights, by Mrs. Shackelford Miller, Pub. by National Society of Colonial Dames in the Commonwealth of Kentucky.

Staffordshire Life, March 1952, *Staffordshire Connections with the United States,* by J. Sidney Horne, and in the same issue, *Gunston Hall,* Mrs. Wakefield of Breewood.

Pamphlet, *Ancient Breewood,* Mary E. Wakefield.

Letter from Mary E. Wakefield.

Appleton's Journal April 4, 1874, Article by John Esten Cooke, Page 417.

Appendix

THE VIRGINIA DECLARATION OF RIGHTS

A DECLARATION of RIGHTS *made by the representatives of the good people of Virginia, assembled in full and free Convention; which rights do pertain to them, and their posterity, as the basis and foundation of government.*

1. THAT all men are by nature equally free and independent, and have certain inherent rights, of which, when they enter into a state of society, they cannot, by any compact, deprive or divest their posterity; namely, the enjoyment of life and liberty, with the means of acquiring and possessing property, and pursuing and obtaining happiness and safety.

2. That all power is vested in, and consequently derived from, the people; that magistrates are their trustees and servants, and at all times amenable to them.

3. That government is, or ought to be, instituted for the common benefit, protection and security, of the people, nation, or community, of all the various modes and forms of government that is best, which is capable of producing the greatest degree of happiness and safety, and is most effectually secured against the danger of mal-administration; and that whenever any government shall be found inadequate or contrary to these purposes, a majority of the community hath an indubitable, unalienable, and indefeasible right, to reform, alter, or abolish it, in such manner as shall be judged most conducive to the publick weal.

[235]

4. That no man, or set of men, are entitled to exclusive or separate emoluments or privileges from the community, but in consideration of publick services; which, not being descendible, neither ought the office of magistrate, legislator, or judge, to be hereditary.

5. That the legislative and executive powers of the state should be separate and distinct from the judiciary; and that the members of the two first may be restrained from oppression, by feeling and participating the burthens of the people, they should, at fixed periods, be reduced to a private station, return into that body from which they were originally taken, and the vacancies be supplied by frequent, certain, and regular elections, in which all, or any part of the former members, to be again eligible, or ineligible, as the laws shall direct.

6. That elections of members to serve as representatives of the people, in assembly, ought to be free; and that all men, having sufficient evidence of permanent common interest with, and attachment to, the community, have the right of suffrage, and cannot be taxed or deprived of their property for publick uses without their own consent, or that of their representatives so elected, nor bound by any law to which they have not, in like manner, assented, for the publick good.

7. That all power of suspending laws, or the execution of laws, by any authority without consent of the representatives of the people, is injurious to their rights, and ought not to be exercised.

8. That in all capital or criminal prosecutions a man hath a right to demand the cause and nature of his accusation, to be confronted with the accusers and witnesses, to call for evidence in his favour, and to a speedy trial by an impartial jury of his vicinage, without whose unanimous consent he cannot be found guilty, nor can he be compelled to give evidence against himself; that no man be deprived of his liberty except by the law of the land, or the judgment of his peers.

9. That excessive bail ought not to be required, nor excessive fines imposed, nor cruel and unusual punishments inflicted.

10. That general warrants, whereby any officer or messenger may be commanded to search suspected places without evidence of a fact committed, or to seize any person or persons not named, or whose offense is not particularly described and supported by evidence, are grievous and oppressive, and ought not to be granted.

11. That in controversies respecting property, and in suits between man and man, the ancient trial by jury is preferable to any other, and ought to be held sacred.

12. That the freedom of the press is one of the great bulwarks of liberty, and can never be restrained but by despotick governments.

13. That a well regulated militia, composed of the body of the people, trained to arms, is the proper, natural, and safe defense of a free state; that standing armies, in time of peace, should be avoided, as dangerous to liberty; and that, in all cases, the military should be under strict subordination to, and governed by, the civil power.

14. That the people have a right to uniform government; and, therefore, that no government separate them, or independent of, the government of *Virginia,* ought to be erected or established within the limits thereof.

15. That no free government, or the blessing of liberty, can be preserved to any people but by a firm adherence to justice, moderation, temperance, frugality, and virtue, and by frequent recurrence to fundamental principles.

16. That religion, or the duty which we owe to our CREATOR, and the manner of discharging it, can be directed only by reason and conviction, not by force or violence, and therefore all men are equally entitled to the free exercise of religion, according to the dictates of conscience; and that it is the mutual duty of all to practice Christian forbearance, love, and charity, towards each other.

THE FAIRFAX COUNTY RESOLVES

The draft of the Resolutions in the handwriting of George Mason, found among the Washington papers ends with the 24th Resolution. A copy preserved in the State Library, Richmond, from which this is taken has the two additional ones appointing the Fairfax County Committee.

At a General Meeting of the Freeholders and other Inhabitants of the County of Fairfax, at the Court House, in the town of Alexandria, on Monday, the 18th day of July, 1774.

George Washington, Esq:, Chairman, and Robert Harrison, Gentleman, Clerk:

1. *Resolved,* That this Colony and Dominion of Virginia cannot be considered as a conquered county, and, if it was, that the present inhabitants are not of the conquered, but of the conquerors. That the same was not settled at the national expense of England, but at the private expense of the adventurers, our ancestors, by solemn compact with, and under the auspices and protection of, the British Crown, upon which we are, in every respect as dependent as the people of Great Britain, and in the same manner subject to all his Majesty's just, legal and constitutional prerogatives; that our ancestors, when they left their native land, and settled in America, brought with them, even if the same had not been confirmed by Charters, the civil constitution and form of Government of the country they came from, and were by the laws of nature and nations entitled to all its privileges, immunities, and advantages, which have descended to us, their posterity, and ought of right to be as fully enjoyed as if we had still continued within the realm of England.

2. *Resolved,* That the most important and valuable part of the British Constitution, upon which its very existence depends, is, the fundamental principle of the people's being governed by no laws to which they have not given their consent by Representatives freely chosen by themselves, who are affected by the laws they enact equally with their constituents, to whom they are accountable, and whose burthens they share, in which consists the safety and happiness of the community; for if this part of

the Constitution was taken away, or materially altered, the government must degenerate either into an absolute and despotic monarchy, or a tyrannical aristocracy, and the freedom of the people be annihilated.

3. *Resolved*, Therefore, as the inhabitants of the American colonies are not, and from their situation, cannot be represented in the British Parliament, that the Legislative power can, of right, be exercised only by our Provincial Assemblies, or Parliaments, subject to the assent or negative of the British Crown, to be declared within some proper limited time; but as it was thought just and reasonable that the people of Great Britain should reap advantages from the colonies adequate to the protection they afforded them, the British Parliament have claimed and exercised the power of regulating our trade and commerce, so as to restrain our importing from foreign countries such articles as they could furnish us with of their own growth and manufacture, or exporting to foreign countries such articles and portions of our produce as Great Britain stood in need of, for her own consumption or manufacture. Such a power directed with wisdom and moderation seems necessary for the general good of that great body politic of which we are a part, although in some degree repugnant to the principles of the Constitution. Under this idea, our ancestors submitted to it, the experience of more than a century during the government of his Majesty's royal predecessors hath proved its utility, and the reciprocal benefits flowing from it produced mutual uninterrupted harmony and good will between the inhabitants of Great Britain and her colonies who during that long period always considered themselves as one and the same people; and though such a power is capable of abuse, and in some instances hath been stretched beyond the original design and institution, yet to avoid strife and contention with our fellow-subjects, and strongly impressed with the experience of mutual benefits, we always cheerfully acquiesced in it while the entire regulation of our internal policy, and giving and granting our own money, were preserved to our own Provincial Legislatures.

4. *Resolved*, That it is the duty of these Colonies, on all emer-

gencies, to contribute in proportion to their abilities, situation, and circumstances, to the necessary charge of supporting and defending the British Empire of which they are a part; that while we are treated upon an equal footing with our fellow-subjects, the motives of self-interest and preservation will be a sufficient obligation, as was evident through the course of the last war; and that no argument can be fairly applied to the British Parliament's taxing us, upon a presumption that we should refuse a just and reasonable contribution, but will equally operate in justification of the Executive Power taxing the people of England, upon a supposition of their Representatives refusing to grant the necessary supplies.

5. *Resolved,* That the claim, lately assumed and exercised by the British Parliament, of making all such laws as they think fit, to govern the people of these colonies, and to extort from us our money without our consent, is not only diametrically contrary to the first principles of the Constitution, and the original compacts by which we are dependent upon the British Crown and government; but is totally incompatible with the privileges of a free people and the natural rights of mankind, will render our own legislatures merely nominal and nugatory, and is calculated to reduce us from a state of freedom and happiness to slavery and misery.

6. *Resolved,* That taxation and representation are in their nature inseparable; that the right of withholding, or of giving and granting their own money, is the only effectual security to a free people against the encroachments of despotism and tyranny; and that whenever they yield the one, they must quickly fall a prey to the other.

7. *Resolved,* That the powers over the people of America now claimed by the British House of Commons, in whose election we have no share, on whose determinations we can have no influence, whose information must be always defective and false, who in many instances may have a separate, and in some an opposite interest to ours, and who are removed from those impressions of tenderness and compassion arising from personal intercourse and

connexions, which soften the rigors of the most despotic governments, must, if continued, establish the most grievous and intolerable species of tyranny and oppression, that ever was inflicted
upon mankind.

8. *Resolved,* That it is our greatest wish and inclination, as well
as interest, to continue our connexion with, and dependence upon,
the British government; but though we are its subjects, we will
use every means, which Heaven hath given us, to prevent our
becoming its slaves.

9. *Resolved,* That there is a premeditated design and system,
formed and pursued by the British ministry, to introduce an
arbitrary government into his Majesty's American dominions; to
which end they are artfully prejudicing our sovereign, and in-
flaming the minds of our fellow-subjects in Great Britain, by
propagating the most malevolent falsehoods, particularly that
there is an intention in the American colonies to set up for independent States; endeavouring at the same time, by various acts
of violence and oppression, by sudden and repeated dissolutions
of our Assemblies, whenever they presume to examine the ille-
gality of ministerial mandates, or deliberate on the violated rights
of their constituents, and by breaking in upon the American
charters, to reduce us to a state of desperation, and dissolve the
original compacts by which our ancestors bound themselves and
their posterity to remain dependent upon the British crown;
which measures unless effectually counteracted, will end in the
ruin both of Great Britain and her colonies.

10. *Resolved,* That the several acts of Parliament for raising a
revenue upon the people of America without their consent, the
creating new and dangerous jurisdictions here, the taking away
our trials by jury, the ordering persons, upon criminal accusa-
tions, to be tried in another country than that in which the fact
is charged to have been committed, the act inflicting ministerial
vengeance upon the town of Boston, and the two bills lately
brought into Parliament for abrogating the charter of the province
of Massachusetts Bay, and for the protection and encouragement
of murderers in the said province, are part of the above mentioned

iniquitous system. That the inhabitants of the town of Boston are now suffering in the common cause of all British America, and are justly entitled to its support and assistance; and therefore that a subscription ought immediately to be opened, and proper persons appointed in every county of this colony to purchase provisions, and consign them to some gentleman of character in Boston, to be distributed among the poorer sort of people there.

11. *Resolved,* That we will cordially join with our friends and brethren of this and the other colonies, in such measures as shall be judged most effectual for procuring redress of our grievances, and that upon obtaining such redress, if the destruction of the tea at Boston be regarded as an invasion of private property, we shall be willing to contribute towards paying the East India Company the value; but as we consider the said Company as the tools and instruments of oppression in the hands of government, and the cause of our present distress, it is the opinion of this meeting, that the people of these colonies should forbear all further dealings with them, by refusing to purchase their merchandise, until that peace, safety, and good order, which they have disturbed be perfectly restored. And that all tea now in this colony, or which shall be imported into it shipped before the 1st day of September next, should be deposited in some storehouse to be appointed by the respective committees of each county, until a sufficient sum of money be raised by subscription to reimburse the owners the value, and then to be publicly burned and destroyed; and if the same is not paid for and destroyed as aforesaid, that it remain in the custody of the said committees, at the risk of the owners, until the act of Parliament imposing a duty upon tea, for raising a revenue in America, be repealed; and immediately afterwards be delivered unto the several proprietors thereof, their agents, or attorneys.

12. *Resolved,* That nothing will so much contribute to defeat the pernicious designs of the common enemies of Great Britain and her colonies, as a firm union of the latter, who ought to regard every act of violence or oppression inflicted upon any one

of them, as aimed at all; and to effect this desirable purpose, that a Congress should be appointed, to consist of deputies from all the colonies, to concert a general and uniform plan for the defense and preservation of our common rights, and continuing the connexion and dependence of the said colonies upon Great Britain, under a just, lenient, permanent, and constitutional form of government.

13. *Resolved,* That our most sincere and cordial thanks be given to the patrons and friends of liberty in Great Britain, for their spirited and patriotic conduct, in support of our constitutional rights and privileges, and their generous efforts to prevent the distress and calamity of America.

14. *Resolved,* That every little jarring interest and dispute, which has ever happened between these colonies, should be buried in eternal oblivion; that all manner of luxury and extravagance ought immediately to be laid aside, as totally inconsistent with the threatening and gloomy prospect before us; that it is the indispensable duty of all the gentlemen and men of fortune to set examples of temperance, fortitude, frugality, and industry, and give every encouragement in their power, particularly by subscriptions and premiums, to the improvement of arts and manufactures in America; that great care and attention should be had to the cultivation of flax, cotton, and other materials for manufactures; and we recommend it to such of the inhabitants, as have large stocks of sheep, to sell to their neighbors at a moderate price, as the most certain means of speedily increasing our breed of sheep, and quantity of wool.

15. *Resolved,* That until American grievances be redressed, by restoration of our just rights and privileges, no goods or merchandise whatsoever ought to be imported into this colony, which shall be shipped from Great Britain or Ireland after the 1st day of September next, except linens not exceeding fifteen pence per yard, coarse woolen cloth, not exceeding two shillings sterling per yard, nails, wire and wire cards, needles and pins, paper, saltpetre, and medicines, which may be imported until the 1st day of September, 1775; and if any goods or merchandise, other than

these hereby excepted, should be shipped from Great Britain, after the time aforesaid, to this colony, that the same immediately upon their arrival, should either be sent back again, by the owners, their agents or attorneys, or stored and deposited in some warehouse, to be appointed by the committee for each respective county, and there kept at the risk and charge of the owners, to be delivered to them, when a free importation of goods hither shall again take place. And that the merchants and venders of goods and merchandise within this colony ought not to take advantage of our present distress, but continue to sell the goods and merchandise which they now have, or which may be shipped to them before the 1st day of September next, at the same rates and prices they have been accustomed to do, within one year last past; and if any person shall sell such goods on any other terms than above expressed, that no inhabitant of this colony should at any time, forever thereafter, deal with him, his agent, factor, or storekeepers for any commodity whatsoever.

16. *Resolved,* That it is the opinion of this meeting, that the merchants and venders of goods and merchandise within this colony should take an oath, not to sell or dispose of any goods or merchandise whatsoever, which may be shipped from Great Britain after the 1st day of September next as aforesaid, except the articles before excepted, and that they will, upon receipt of such prohibited goods, either send the same back again by the first opportunity, or deliver them to the committees in the respective counties, to be deposited in some warehouse, at the risk and charge of the owners, until they, their agents, or factors, be permitted to take them away by the said committees; the names of those who refuse to take such oath to be advertised by the respective committees in the counties wherein they reside. And to the end that the inhabitants of this colony may know what merchants and venders of goods and merchandise have taken such oath, that the respective committees should grant a certificate thereof to every such person who shall take the same.

17. *Resolved,* That it is the opinion of this meeting, that during our present difficulties and distress, no slaves ought to be im-

ported into any of the British colonies on this continent; and we take this opportunity of declaring our most earnest wishes to see an entire stop forever put to such a wicked, cruel, and unnatural trade.

18. *Resolved,* That no kind of lumber should be exported from this colony to the West Indies, until America be restored to her constitutional rights and liberties, if the other colonies will accede to a like resolution; and that it be recommended to the general Congress to appoint as early a day as possible for stopping such export.

19. *Resolved,* That it is the opinion of this meeting, if American grievances be not redressed before the 1st day of November, 1775, that all exports of produce from the several colonies to Great Britain should cease; and to carry the said resolution more effectually into execution, that we will not plant or cultivate any tobacco, after the crop now growing; provided the same measure shall be adopted by the other colonies on this continent, as well those who have heretofore made tobacco, as those who have not. And it is our opinion also, if the Congress of deputies from the several colonies shall adopt the measure of non-exportation to Great Britain, as the people will be thereby disabled from paying their debts, that no judgments should be rendered by the courts in the said colonies for any debt, after information of the said measure's being determined upon.

20. *Resolved,* That it is the opinion of this meeting that a solemn covenant and assocation should be entered into by the inhabitants of all the colonies upon oath, that they will not, after the times which shall be respectively agreed on at the general Congress, export any manner of lumber to the West Indies, nor any of their produce to Great Britain, or sell or dispose of the same to any person who shall not have entered into the said covenant and association; and also that they will not import or receive any goods or merchandise which shall be shipped from Great Britain after the 1st day of September next, other than the before enumerated articles, nor buy or purchase any goods except as before excepted, of any person whatsoever, who shall not have

taken the oath herein before recommended to be taken by the merchants and venders of goods; nor buy or purchase any slaves hereafter imported into any part of this continent, until a free exportation and importation be again resolved on by a majority of the representatives or deputies of the colonies. And that the respective committees of the counties, in each colony, so soon as the covenant and association becomes general, publish by advertisements in their several counties, a list of the names of those (if any such there be) who will not accede thereto; that such traitors to their country may be publicly known and detested.

21. *Resolved,* That it is the opinion of this meeting that this and the other associating colonies should break off all trade, intercourse, and dealings, with that colony, province, or town, which shall decline or refuse to agree to the plan, which shall be adopted by the general Congress.

22. *Resolved,* That should the town of Boston be forced to submit to the late and cruel and oppressive measures of government, that we shall not hold the same to be binding upon us, but will, notwithstanding, religiously maintain and inviolably adhere to such measures as shall be concerted by the general Congress, for the preservation of our lives, liberties, and fortunes.

23. *Resolved,* That it be recommended to the deputies of the general Congress, to draw up and transmit an humble and dutiful petition and remonstrance to his Majesty, asserting with decent firmness our just and constitutional rights and privileges; lamenting the fatal necessity of being compelled to enter into measures disgusting to his Majesty and his Parliament, or injurious to our fellow-subjects in Great Britain; declaring, in the strongest terms, our duty and affection to his Majesty's person, family, and government, and our desire to continue our dependence upon Great Britain; and most humbly conjuring and beseeching his Majesty not to reduce his faithful subjects of America to a state of desperation, and to reflect, that from our sovereign there can be but one appeal. And it is the opinion of this meeting, that after such petition and remonstrance shall have been presented to his Majesty, the same should be printed in the public papers, in all the principal towns in Great Britain.

24. *Resolved,* That George Washington and George Broadwater, lately elected our representatives to serve in the General Assembly, be appointed to attend the Convention at Williamsburg on the 1st day of August next, and present these Resolves, as the sense of the people of this county, upon the measures proper to be taken in the present alarming and dangerous situation of America.

25. *Resolved,* That George Washington, Esqr., John West, George Mason, William Ramsay, William Rumney, George Gilpin, Rob. Hanson Harrison, John Carlyle, Robt. Adam, John Dalton, Philip Alexander, James Kirk, William Brown, Charles Broadwater, William Payne, Martin Cockburn, Lee Massey, William Hartshorne, Thos. Triplett, Charles Alexander, Thomas Pollard, Townshend Dade, Jr., Edward Payne, Henry Gunnell, and Thomas Lewis, be a committee for this county; that they or a majority of them, on any emergency, have power to call a general meeting, and to concert and adopt such measures as may be thought most expedient and necessary.

26. *Resolved,* That a copy of these proceedings be transmitted to the printers at Williamsburg to be published.

Robt. Harrison, Clerk.

THE DECLARATION OF INDEPENDENCE

When in the Course of human events, it becomes necessary for one people to dissolve the political bands which have connected them with another, and to assume among the powers of the earth, the separate and equal station to which the Laws of Nature and of Nature's God entitle them, a decent respect to the opinions of mankind requires that they should declare the causes which impel them to the separation.

We hold these truths to be self-evident, that all men are created equal, that they are endowed by their Creator with certain unalienable Rights, that among these are Life, Liberty and the pursuit of Happiness.—That to secure these rights, Governments are instituted among Men, deriving their just powers from the consent of the governed.—That whenever any

Form of Government becomes destructive of these ends, it is the Right of the People to alter or to abolish it, and to institute new Government, laying its foundation on such principles and organizing its powers in such form, as to them shall seem most likely to effect their Safety and Happiness. Prudence, indeed, will dictate that Governments long established should not be changed for light and transient causes; and accordingly all experience hath shewn, that mankind are more disposed to suffer, while evils are sufferable, than to right themselves by abolishing the forms to which they are accustomed. But when a long train of abuses and usurpations, pursuing invariably the same Object evinces a design to reduce them under absolute Despotism, it is their right, it is their duty, to throw off such Government, and to provide new Guards for their future security.—Such has been the patient sufferance of these Colonies; and such is now the necessity which constrains them to alter their former Systems of Government. The history of the present King of Great Britain is a history of repeated injuries and usurpations, all having in direct object the establishment of an absolute Tyranny over these States. To prove this, let Facts be submitted to a candid world.

He has refused his Assent to Laws, the most wholesome and necessary for the public good.

He has forbidden his Governors to pass Laws of immediate and pressing importance, unless suspended in their operation till his Assent should be obtained; and when so suspended, he has utterly neglected to attend to them.

He has refused to pass other Laws for the accommodation of large districts of people, unless those people would relinquish the right of Representation in the Legislature, a right inestimable to them and formidable to tyrants only.

He has called together legislative bodies at places unusual, uncomfortable, and distant from the depository of their public Records, for the sole purpose of fatiguing them into compliance with his measures.

He has dissolved Representative Houses repeatedly for opposing with manly firmness his invasions on the rights of the people.

He has refused for a long time, after such dissolutions, to cause others to be elected; whereby the Legislative powers, incapable of Annihilation, have returned to the People at large for their exercise; the State remaining in the meantime exposed to all the dangers of invasion from without, and convulsions within.

He has endeavored to prevent the population of these States; for that purpose obstructing the Laws for Naturalization of Foreigners; refusing to pass others to encourage their migrations hither, and raising the conditions of new Appropriations of Lands.

He has obstructed the Administration of Justice, by refusing his Assent to Laws for establishing Judiciary powers.

He has made Judges dependent on his Will alone, for the tenure of their offices, and the amount and payment of their salaries.

He has erected a multitude of New Offices, and sent hither swarms of Officers to harrass our people, and eat out their substance.

He has kept among us, in times of peace, Standing Armies without the Consent of our legislatures.

He has affected to render the Military independent of and superior to the Civil power.

He has combined with others to subject us to a jurisdiction foreign to our constitution and unacknowledged by our laws, giving his Assent to their Acts of pretended Legislation:—For quartering large bodies of armed troops among us:—For protecting them, by a mock Trial, from punishment for any Murders which they should commit on the Inhabitants of these States:—For cutting off our Trade with all parts of the world:—For imposing Taxes on us without our Consent:—For depriving us in many cases, of the benefits of Trial by Jury:—For transporting us beyond Seas to be tried for pretended offenses:—For abolishing the free System of English Laws in a neighboring Province, establishing therein an Arbitrary government, and enlarging its Boundaries so as to render it at once an example and fit instrument for introducing the same absolute rule into these Colonies:— For taking away our Charters, abolishing our most valuable Laws, and altering fundamentally the Forms of our Governments:—For suspending our own Legislatures and declaring themselves invested with power to legislate for us in all cases whatsoever.

He has abdicated Government here, by declaring us out of his Protection and waging War against us.

He has plundered our seas, ravished our Coasts, burnt our towns, and destroyed the lives of our people.

He is at this time transporting large Armies of foreign Mercenaries to compleat the works of death, desolation and tyranny, already begun with circumstances of Cruelty and perfidy scarely paralleled in the most barbarous ages, and totally unworthy the Head of a civilized nation.

He has contrained our fellow Citizens taken Captive on the high Seas to bear Arms against their Country, to become the executioners of their friends and Brethren, or to fall themselves by their Hands.

He has excited domestic insurrections amongst us, and has endeavored to bring on the inhabitants of our frontiers, the merciless Indian Savages, whose known rule of warfare, is an undistinguished destruction of all ages, sexes and conditions. In every stage of these Oppressions We have Petitioned for Redress in the most humble terms: Our repeated Petitions have been answered only by repeated injury. A Prince, whose character is thus marked by every act which may define a Tyrant, is unfit to be the ruler of a free people. Nor have we been wanting in attentions to our Brittish brethren. We have warned them from time to time of attempts by their legislature to extend an unwarrantable jurisdiction over us. We have reminded them of the circumstances of our emigration and settlement here. We have appealed to their native justice and magnanimity, and we have conjured them by the ties of our common kindred to disavow these usurpations, which, would inevitably interrupt our connections and correspondence. They too have been deaf to the voice of justice and of consanguinity. We must, therefore, acquiesce in the necessity, which denounces our Separation, and hold them, as we hold the rest of mankind, Enemies in War, in Peace Friends.

We, therefore, the Representatives of the united States of America, in General Congress, Assembled, appealing to the Supreme Judge of the world for the rectitude of our intentions do, in the Name, and by authority of the good People of these Colonies, solemnly publish and declare, That these United Colonies are, and of Right ought to be, Free and Independent States; that they are Absolved from all Allegiance to the British Crown, and that all political connection between them and the State of Great Britain, is and ought to be totally dissolved; and that as Free and Independent States, they have full Power to levy War, conclude Peace, contract Alliances, establish Commerce, and do all other Acts and Things which Independent States may of right do. And for the support of this Declaration, with a firm reliance on the protection of divine Providence, we mutually pledge to each other our Lives, our Fortunes and our sacred Honor.

NEW HAMPSHIRE

Josiah Bartlett
Wm. Whipple
Matthew Thornton

VIRGINIA

George Wythe
Richard Henry Lee
Th. Jefferson
Benja. Harrison
Thos. Nelson, jr.
Francis Lightfoot Lee
Carter Braxton

RHODE ISLAND

Step. Hopkins
William Ellery
Fras. Hopkinson
John Hart
Abra. Clark

MASSACHUSETTS

John Hancock
Saml. Adams
John Adams
Robt. Treat Paine
Elbridge Gerry

CONNECTICUT

Roger Sherman
Sam'el Huntington
Wm. Williams
Oliver Wolcott

NEW YORK

Wm. Floyd
Phil. Livingston
Frans. Lewis
Lewis Morris

GEORGIA

Button Gwinnett
Lyman Hall
Geo. Walton

PENNSYLVANIA

Robt. Morris
Benjamin Rush
Benja. Franklin
John Morton
Geo. Clymer
Jas. Smith
Geo. Taylor
James Wilson
Geo. Ross

SOUTH CAROLINA

Edward Rutledge
Thos. Heyward, Junr.
Thomas Lynch, Junr.
Arthur Middleton

MARYLAND

Samuel Chase
Wm. Paca
Thos. Stone
Charles Carroll of
*   Carrollton*

NORTH CAROLINA

Wm. Hooper
Joseph Hewes
John Penn

DELAWARE

Caesar Rodney
Geo. Read
Tho. M'Kean

NEW JERSEY

Richd. Stockton
Jno. Witherspoon

The signatures are arranged according to states, not in the order in which they appeared on the original document.

THE BILL OF RIGHTS

The first ten Amendments to the Constitution, proposed by
Congress September, 1789 and certified as adopted
December 15, 1791

I. Congress shall make no law respecting an establishment of religion, or prohibiting the free exercise thereof; or abridging the freedom of speech, or of the press; or the right of the people peaceably to assemble, and to petition the Government for a redress of grievances.

II. A well regulated Militia being necessary to the security of a free State, the right of the people to keep and bear Arms, shall not be infringed.

III. No soldier shall, in time of peace be quartered in any house, without the consent of the Owner, nor in time of war, but in a manner to be prescribed by law.

IV. The right of the people to be secure in their persons, houses, papers, and effects, against unreasonable searches and seizures, shall not be violated, and no Warrants shall issue, but upon probable cause, supported by Oath or affirmation, and particularly describing the place to be searched, and the persons or things to be seized.

V. No person shall be held to answer for a capital, or otherwise infamous crime, unless on a presentment or indictment of a Grand Jury, except in cases arising in the land or naval forces, or in the Militia, when in actual service in time of War or public danger; nor shall any person be subject for the same offense to be twice put in jeopardy of life or limb, nor shall be compelled in any criminal case to be a witness against himself, nor be deprived of life, liberty, or property, without due process of law; nor shall private property be taken for public use, without just compensation.

VI. In all criminal prosecutions, the accused shall enjoy the right to a speedy and public trial, by an impartial jury of the State and district wherein the crime shall have been committed, which district shall have been previously ascertained by law, and to be informed of the nature and cause of the accusation; to be confronted with the witnesses against him; to have compulsory process for obtaining Witnesses in his favor, and to have the Assistance of Counsel for his defense.

VII. In Suits at common law, where the value in controversy shall exceed twenty dollars, the right of trial by jury shall be preserved, and no fact tried by a jury, shall be otherwise re-examined in any Court of the United States, than according to the rules of the common law.

VIII. Excessive bail shall not be required, nor excessive fines imposed, nor cruel and unusual punishments inflicted.

IX. The enumeration in the Constitution, of certain rights, shall not be construed to deny or disparage others retained by the people.

X. The powers not delegated to the United States by the Constitution, nor prohibited by it to the States, are reserved to the States respectively, or to the people.

THE PRESIDENT'S OATH OF OFFICE

I do solemnly swear (or affirm) that I will faithfully execute the Office of President of the United States, and will to the best of my Ability preserve, protect and defend the Constitution of the United States.

The Constitution of the United States, Art. II—Sec. I.